If Ponies Rode Men

The Journeys of Robert Land, 1777–1791

JAMES ELLIOTT

Original illustrations by Juanita Mitchell

"Robert Land on Little Lake"
Cover painting by Peter Rindlisbacher

Design: MakinToth Design

Printer: Barrie Press Inc.

Published 1999 by
the Stoney Creek Historical Society
P.O. Box 66637
Stoney Creek, Ontario
L8G 5E5

ISBN 0-9686139-0-X

Printed in Canada

The author would like to acknowledge help lent this project by a number of individuals. Sincere thanks are due: University of Chicago Press editor, Barbara Sivertsen for informed comment, Robert Land descendent and Land family historian Brian Land for interest and support, historians Don and Diane Graves for guidance, novelist Douglas Glover for direction and the late John Coleman, for all his kindnesses. Sally Talaga of the Wayne County Historical Society in Honesdale, PA for access to records, Mary Curtis of the National Parks Service in Milanville for an expert guided tour of the Upper Delaware, Christopher Moore for Loyalist background, Doug Hendry for archival work, Bill McNeil for maritime expertise, Violet Shawanda for central Ojibway translation and of course, the executive of the Stoney Creek Historical Society for its forbearance. To my wife Irene, who endured more than two years of Robert Land living in our basement, I owe the greatest debt.

CONTENTS

Prologue

Noted American historian John M. Coleman mounted the first intensive search for Robert Land more than four decades ago. After combing archival sources on both sides of the border he was forced to make the following admission. The subject, he wrote, "remains obscured in a fog of pious, albeit conflicting legends and there are few facts about him that are not open to question. We would like to know more but unfortunately he left behind only the records that a man cannot help leaving."

Indeed.

Faithfully reconstituting Robert Land from the surviving fragments of history is like trying to recreate a unique piece of pottery from a few shards.

Many readers will of course be familiar with the romantic version of the Land saga. The family burned out and presumed dead. Land, exiled to the wilds of Lake Ontario until a totally unexpected reunion occurs several years later. This version, celebrated in poetry and prose, has enjoyed considerable currency in Hamilton since the Land family story first saw print in 1869. Although it bears some resemblance to what likely occurred there are many major points of departure.

What we know about Robert Land and his family can be briefly stated. He was born in New York state in 1738 and enlisted to fight against the French in 1758, the same year his first son, John was born. He settled in the Delaware Valley—as early as 1756—and was subsequently appointed magistrate, a position he still held when the 13 colonies broke with England in 1775. The origins of his wife Phoebe are less certain. Born in 1733, she would bear at least eight children between 1757 and 1777.

Beyond those facts there is a series of sporadic sightings of the Lands at various times throughout the Revolution. They are tantalizing but fall far short of any kind of a comprehensive picture. What is known is that he one of Brant's Volunteers and worked as a spy and recruiter for the British Indian Department in Pennsylvania and New York. He escaped a death sentence for treason and was wounded in another skirmish. Used as a courier between New York, Fort Niagara, Montreal and Quebec, Land was drawing supplies from Fort Niagara some years after the war ended.

Given the dearth of details the complete story of Robert Land can only be a matter of speculation. As the French scholar Charles-Victor Langlois wrote: "No documents, no history."

And yet the story endures and is so much a part of the lore of early Hamilton that it demands to be told.

How then to deal with all the gaps that occur in the record without turning the Land saga into a novel?

Reassemble the surviving shards and render the shape credibly whole with new clay drawn from contextual evidence and contemporary accounts. The historical record provides the framework of the story, no characters or major events have been invented although the eighth Land child has been given a name.

The burning of the Land homestead remains. Although no solid proof that it actually occurred came to light, circumstantial evidence indicates it did.

The resulting narrative can never claim to be definitive, indeed such an account seems unlikely unless a Robert Land diary were to surface. Instead what's offered is a plausible account of what might have happened based on the evidence and the context of the times. Not the absolute account but a defensible account. Perhaps some will take issue, certainly the debate is welcome.

American readers may be surprised, and perhaps irritated, to find an account of the Revolution seen through the eyes of the other side. The fact is though, the Patriots won the propaganda war long before they won the real war and cast the Loyalists as villains, an American stereotype that endures to this day despite considerable evidence to the contrary. For Loyalists like Robert Land there is no pretense of objectivity in their view of history, only the bitter reality of exile and forfeit lives. To them, the Rebels are the oppressors.

The challenge was to produce a narrative account of Robert Land solidly based on the available historical evidence. To stay within the framework of the known facts—as awkward and implausible as they seem at times—while at the same time fleshing out the bones of history with some recognizably human characters.

To animate Robert Land and the extraordinary times through which he lived. His story—as a refugee fleeing from war—should find some resonance in contemporary times. If, in some small way it succeeds, then the effort was worthwhile.

Quoted passages have been imagined, except where they are taken verbatim from court transcripts, correspondence and petitions. Likewise the letters printed are not originals, but composites based on surviving letters and rendered in the style of the time.

The quotes that preface every chapter are genuine, drawn from contemporary sources, some directly relating to the Land saga—transcripts, petitions, letters—and some from general sources that convey a sentiment or observation pertinent to the story.

The story of Robert Land is not appreciably different from that of thousands of Loyalists. In their human struggles of hope and loss are echoes of our own lives.

May, 1784

ℂƵ

"Wretches so disgraced with infamy and crimes…"
—Albany County resolution

A birch canoe glides along the lakeward side of a curiously narrow strip of beach, the man in the stern turning to look through the waving grass and stunted oaks.

He's lithe and dark with a seasoned face and deep-set eyes. The hair, under a broad-brimmed hat, is long and tied back in a queue.

Small waves beat the shore where finch and sparrow chatter. The man stays the paddle to gaze beyond the beach.

One of the British officers at the fort spoke of this sprawling harbour at the head of the lake, a place the Indians call *Wequatetong.* But what he sees beyond this long beach is more like another lake than a harbour.

For three days he's been coasting west from Fort Niagara, exploring the mouths of streams and creeks.

The war that ranged up and down the thirteen colonies for eight years, is over and provincial troops and volunteers, like Robert Land, who have no further military purpose, are striking out to explore the land of their exile.

Exile indeed, all have heard accounts of Loyalist soldiers, bold enough, or foolish enough, to return to homes they'd left during the war, only to be whipped and driven away.

The bitter truth was, Americans like Land, who backed the losing side during the revolution, had been banished and could never go home.

Slowly, new lands west of Niagara River were being opened and refugees of that war were looking for new homes.

One inlet, a 20-mile paddle from Niagara had been promising. Some of Butler's men had already claimed land there but it was just a pond compared to this bay. Sheltered yet large enough to accommodate whole fleets.

A strand of grey sand, matted over with waist-high grass and dotted with groves of squat oaks separates the bay from the lake. Beyond the bay lies the low stony ridge that parallels

the lake all the way from Niagara. The only feature on an otherwise flat expanse of forest.

Land finds the natural outflow that drains the bay, shallow, languid and easily crossed.

Drawing up his paddle he looks to where the bay shallows out in swale and marshland. Beyond that, the land rises in two rolling steps to the rocky spine. Unlike the steep tracts that hem the Delaware this is level land, good for crops.

Crossing the bay, he can see the dark forms of salmon below. Easing his canoe through swatches of wild rice, he works down a narrowing inlet overhung with willows. Three deer, drinking at the water's edge lift their heads. On land, clouds of pigeons dip and wheel above the forest.

At the end of the inlet Land ties off. Shouldering his musket and hunting bag, he steps through the scrub into the cool darkness of the forest.

The war's been over nearly a year, but he still moves with the natural wariness of a fugitive.

Starved of light, there is little undergrowth on the forest floor and he moves easily through ferns and white lilies.

Beneath the luminous canopy grander than any church Land saw in New York, the air is damp, heavy with the earthy smell of leaf mould. The forest hums with insect and bird song.

He is struck by the familiarity of this forest, so similar to the great timber stands along the Delaware he helped harvest and raft downriver to Philadelphia. With the eye of a woodturner he surveys walnut and basswood and sees sturdy furniture. But mostly he sees a vast spread of bottom land a hundred times the size of the river flats he's left behind.

The terrain is not flat but rolls and rises gently. Several creeks have carved ravines that snake down to the bay. Occasionally there are open grasslands, perhaps the result of a fire break or an ancient beaver meadow.

Topping a small rise in one of these meadows, Land stops to rest and watch a large rattlesnake slither away. He cuts a twist of dark tobacco, tucks it into a stained clay pipe and tops it with a knot of flax. Steel and flint collide in a shower of sparks, he draws deeply, pulling fire into the bowl.

Surveying a nearby grove of beech trees, Land rubs a pinch of the rich black earth between his thumb and forefinger and nods. Corn, squash, beans and maybe even a little wheat on the higher ground.

There is promise in this new land, already in his mind he can see a cabin and corn crib, perhaps a stable…

So much to gain…

But so much lost…

The pipe slips from his hand and a jumble of images flash with the intensity of lightning—each full of sharp pain and sorrow.

His youngest son's dirty grey burial shroud—*Dear Will, you knew nothing but war and want*—the charred remains of the Delaware homestead—*15 years of labour, torched in fear and resentment.* The oldest son, hanged and humiliated like a dog—*Poor John, the price you paid for being first born.* The contorted faces of enemies who once were friends and neighbours—*Robert Land, this court martial sentences you to death for treason.* The lead musket ball that flattened him with the force of a falling tree, the trusting face of his mountain guide, Morden—*flee Land, flee!*—dead at the end of a Rebel rope rightly meant for him. The brave, trembling smile Phoebe had worn the last time he left his family—*Go well Robert, and return to us soon…*

Dizzy and sweating in a sun that has suddenly become unbearably hot and threatening, Land lurches to sprawl facedown in the shade of the beech grove and draw coolness from the dark earth.

So much blood, so much pain. So many widows, so many orphans. In his mind he can hear, rising and falling, the keening wail of the Iroquois death rites. Slowly the pounding in his head begins to subside, his breathing gradually eases and the fevered images begin to fade.

To rest a moment in the cool darkness of this wilderness wood so far from what used to be home, so far from family. And to wonder if life can be restored after so many destructive years…the years of rage and ruin when all the world turned upside down…

April, 1777

ઝ

"And if there were ever a just war…"
—Thomas Paine

The debate becomes war.

It's 1777, fifteen years into the reign of King George III, and long-standing disaffection in His Majesty's American Colonies has boiled over into a cruel and vicious war that is part civil and part revolutionary. The people, who are no longer his subjects, curse the monarch and topple his grand statues.

The thirteen colonies—eight controlled directly by England, three owned by private companies and two self-governing—are almost separate countries, but they have found common cause in their opposition to British rule. The issue has cruelly split their population into three roughly equal parts—Rebels, Tories and neutrals.

This war is about independence. The Patriots fight to attain it. The Loyalists to avoid it.

Ironically those who are the loudest in demanding liberty are the least tolerant of dissent. Those seen as less than wholehearted in their support of independence are deemed to be against it. Those adjudged "inimical to the liberties of America" face persecution, loss of property, violence and exile. Whippings, coats of tar and feathers and fines are common occurrences.

As positions harden, push becomes shove and neighbours, friends and even family members become bitter, often deadly, enemies overnight.

The active Loyalists who are prepared to take a stand, probably number about one-quarter of the two and a half million colonists.

Cities like Boston are the hotbeds of rebellion and even the most ardent Loyalists there fear to speak their minds. In many isolated frontier settlements however, like those along the Mohawk and Delaware River valleys, the urgent sense of growing national identity that animates and motivates urban patriots, is nowhere near as evident. Here opposition to these radical ideas is much stronger, and the uprising, which Patriots like Samuel Adams prefer to characterize as a popular revolution, looks much more like bloody civil war.

Here, 200 miles north of Philadelphia where the Delaware River winds between the Poconos and the Kaatskills, the war has brought hatred and distrust.

Here, in a tiny logging and farming settlement called Cushetunk, the war has riven what was a tightly knit community.

Near a fording spot at the lower end of Cushetunk, just below the Indian path that runs east to the Hudson and west to the Susquehanna, stands a substantial log house. Facing the river, snug in the lee of a hill, set well back amid a stand of pines, it is hardly visible from the river. The log walls have been shingled with pine, there is real glass in the two windows, ironwork hinges on the front door and split basswood planks on the floor that spreads out from a fieldstone hearth, tall enough to accommodate a standing man. The furniture, though simple, shows the hand of an artisan. In the yard behind the house a tiny brook flows through beds of skunk cabbage and fiddleheads. Off to the side is a stable fenced with cedar rails, a husking peg for drying corn, a smokehouse and a privy. Two pigs nose through the barnyard mud, and a handful of thin chickens forage through the early spring grass around the stable.

A large patch of bottomland stretches from the house to the river.

From the trail that rises behind the house, four armed men on horseback have just descended and one, a weedy, red-head dismounts. He surveys the homestead, steps forward and hammers on the door.

The top part of the Dutch door is opened by a tall, middle-aged woman clutching an infant to her breast, her petticoats flanked by two young girls and two younger boys. She recognizes a former neighbour who now leads the local militia and knows why he's come.

"Phoebe Land," he calls, a rising edge in his voice, "where's your man?"

"Not here, Cap'n Tyler" she answers, pushing the baby further up her shoulder, "he's gone cutting timber with John and Abel."

"Cutting timber are they? he says turning with a mirthless smile to his still-mounted companions. "Or are they out stealing cattle for the monster Brant?

Your husband's a traitor and a spy, Mrs. Land. Everybody knows he recruits for the King. I reckon it's time he was called to account."

Phoebe's eyes blaze for a moment then she drops her gaze, "they're in the bush, I expect they'll be home tonight."

"Well, you tell them the Committee of Public Safety wants to talk

to them. And you tell your neighbour Bryant Kane the same goes for him."

Turning to mount his horse he stops, looks back and points a finger: "Remember one thing Mrs. Land. In case your menfolk are thinking of skulking off to Fort Niagara or that leper's colony, New York. There's a lot of Indios and rough characters along this river. Harm could come to a family without its menfolk."

Late that night Robert Land returns to find Phoebe sitting in the boilsted rocker he'd made, staring into the hearth. Above them in the loft the children sleep on straw mattresses. Beside the hearth in a pine cradle, the baby snores lightly.

"They came for you today," she says in a flat voice, not looking up from the hearth. "Bezaleel Tyler and his rabble. Said they'd be back in the morning."

"That blowhard Tyler? Captain Mush? He comes back again I've a mind to sic the dogs on him. That's what he merits. Sic 'em on that public safety committee too. Lord how I despise those levellers."

"Robert, he's captain of the militia now…and they say the committee gets its authority direct from the Continental Congress."

"They can all go to the devil, Phoebe. Clinton's in New York City, Burgoyne's in Canada and Brant's on the frontier. Mark my words. We'll crush these Boston puritans. Just you wait."

"Perhaps, but in the meantime we get weasels like Zeal Tyler sniffing around here. It's easy for you Robert, taking John and Abel and going for the King but what are Kate and I to do with a new baby and three young ones?"

And what about those committee judges? They're liable to pack you off to the Simsbury pits. Or worse. I hear they're hanging people in some parts. Either way you'll be precious little use to us."

"Don't you worry about them. I'll just tell them their blueskin spys are mistaken. I have some authority here. After all, I am still a magistrate charged with upholding the King's laws."

"And if they press you to take the oath of allegiance?"

"I guess I'll take it if I must. Not that it means anything what with a trumped up congress trying to speak for thirteen colonies. Might as well try and hitch thirteen cats to a plough."

"You go back on your oath and they'll be out for your blood. You won't be able to stay here, so I suppose that means you'll go with the savage Brant?"

"Phoebe, I must. Unless someone backs off these rogues and skinners, they'll just drive us off and seize our holdings. Besides, Brant's no more savage than these Rebel committeemen who tar and feather anyone who doesn't agree with them."

"Robert, what's going to happen to us? It's not safe here. I hear folks been following the Johnsons to Canada. Is that where we'll end up?"

"I forbid it Phoebe. This is our home and our children's home. We've left too much sweat on this soil to be run off like squatters. If the British find their backbone this war'll be over in a year."

April, 1777

☙

*"You have exceedingly angered me…I shall certainly destroy
without distinction does the like conduct take place in future…"*
—Thayendenegea

"Almost unremittingly on actual service…"
—Brant Volunteer

Joseph Brant is boiling rattlesnake when Land comes into camp. Squatting beside a small driftwood fire in the dawn light, the Mohawk war chief is cutting a small timber rattler into chunks and dropping them into an iron pot.

Tall and wraith-like with a fierce cast to his dark eyes, **The Brant**, looking younger than his 34 years, cuts a curiously elegant figure in the bush. He wears his hair in a scalp-lock but there is nothing rough or savage about his wardrobe. The breech-clout and leggings are cut from fine blue wool. The moccasins trimmed with matching blue wool and decorated with beads. Over a linen shirt, falling mid- thigh, he wears a short, green coat. A shell-shaped, silver gorget hangs around his neck. He wears a trade-silver armband and a gold ring. A dark-blue blanket slung over his shoulder completes the picture.

"Deckart and Hough are both taken with ague," Brant says turning to look at Land, "the pair shaking under their blankets like bones in bags. Some snake broth should restore them."

"I'll stick to wake-me-up if you don't mind," Land replies.

Brant's Destructives, as they're becoming known, are just starting to wake up. For two days they've camped on this little beach beside the Susquehanna awaiting direction from Fort Niagara. The beach borders a bank where maples grow in clumps of four or five from the same stump. In the wake of the spring freshet they provide easy caches of dry firewood.

There are 40 men in camp, a handful are Indians but most are white. They are poor tenant farmers from remote areas along the Delaware who, hounded by Rebel committees, have come to Brant for leadership. And revenge. The Indians, renegade Mohawk and Seneca, are friends and clansmen of Brant.

The white volunteers go against the grain. Most are a decade or two beyond the ideal soldiering years, some are in their 50's, a few are barely teenagers. They have no uniforms and no discipline. Unlike Johnson's and Butler's provincial corps they are neither paid nor equipped by the Crown. Yet they fight with the cruelty and ferocity of wildcats. They live harsh, dangerous lives and face death at the end of a rope if captured.

Thayendenegea, the low-born Iroquois, Christian consort of aristocrat and king, the civilized savage, heathen saint, veteran of the Seven Years' War, the Pontiac rebellion and a staunch Loyalist. He cuts a strange figure on the frontier, this holy heathen, at times a charming and courteous gentlemen, at others, a cold and callous killer.

His independence scares the British. His ferocity terrifies the Americans.

In a strange role reversal his white volunteers are beginning to look more like the savages. They paint their faces and wear breech-clouts, some even shave their heads and have Iroquois tattoos—while the Indians affect linen shirts and beaver hats. To help identify each other in the smoke of battle they wear yellow lace on their headgear.

In a series of daring and destructive raids throughout New York and Pennsylvania, Brant and his fast-moving volunteers have enflamed the frontier and are rapidly becoming the stuff of legend. Already they have been blamed for several outrages they had no part in. Demoralized Rebel militiamen say pursuing Brant's Red & White Volunteers is like trailing a pack of wolves through the woods—extremely difficult and very, very dangerous. Brant's frontier raids are opening wounds that neither side will allow to heal.

Since coming to Brant's standard, Land has been on several raids, but the British Indian Department and military authorities in New York City have other plans for a tough and resourceful woodsman. He's best used as an express, or courier, carrying dispatches and intelligence as far afield as Fort Niagara. This is a role he took up shortly after the war began. He also recruits for the Indian Department working the remote settlements, persuading embittered Loyalists to cast their lots with Brant.

It is hazardous and demanding work. Using the ancient Indian highways that criss-cross Pennsylvania and New York, Land must slip through, not only Rebel American lines but also the territory of their Indian allies, the Oneida.

Trips to Niagara are long and severe, commonly requiring a month's journey on foot in summer, and half as long again by snowshoe in winter. Provisions must be carried. More than once supplies have run short and he's resorted to the Indian trick of cinching in his gut with a leather belt to keep hunger pangs at bay.

Already there have been several narrow escapes. Just last month a house search by Bezaleel Tyler narrowly missed finding dispatches he'd hidden in his ink stand.

Accused of being a Crown sympathizer, Land confronted the Committee of Public Safety, hotly denying accusations he was recruiting for the government, suggesting his detractors were more interested in his fertile and much-improved plantation than the cause of Liberty.

When a neighbour had taken the stand to testify against Land, Phoebe lost her temper, shook her fist and told him he was "as black as hell."

In the end Land had gritted his teeth, repeated the Oath of Allegiance to the United States and been set loose but there were dark looks and muttered threats from local settlers including Bezaleel Tyler who pointed and said "we ain't done with you yet."

Land had left immediately to join Brant, leaving his sons with his family in Cushetunk.

☙

"The most horrid scenes of savage barbarity has been exhibited..."
—Benjamin Tusten

They came 10 days after Land left.

He'd taken the family mare leaving John and Abel to plough and plant on their own. After struggling all day to drag the heavy ploughshare through the clumpy, brown earth they had finished just after sunset.

Phoebe ladles them bowls of succotash and slabs of smoked pork. They talk of the weather—the east wind and the high cloud means rain—before climbing to the loft and collapsing on straw pallets with the rest of the children.

Kate, sleeps in front of the hearth beside William's cradle.

They come as silently as moonlight on a meadow. Kate, who is deep in dreamless sleep, feels something brush the arch of her foot. Instinctively she draws her foot up and turns back to sleep.

Then it comes again.

Forcing her eyes open she can see only a crouching shadow at the foot of the cradle, a shadow that speaks in a hissing whisper.

"Cross river. Warn family."

Without another word the figure withdraws and disappears through the open door.

Rubbing her eyes, Kate struggles to organize her thoughts: The family across the river can only be the Kanes. Bryant Kane, like her father, has gone to the King and left a hired man to watch over his young family.

Drawing the blanket over her chemise, she slips the door. The dew on the grass is cool. Overhead a hazy moon lights the path running to the river where a small bark canoe is tethered. Pulling slowly against the flow, Kate can hear nothing except a chorus of frogs and the soft roar of the downstream rapids. In a few minutes she's pulling the canoe beside a small plank wharf. Following the floodplain path that climbs to the Kane cabin and outbuildings, Kate wonders how she will explain waking the family.

Suddenly she stops. Just before the threshold of the door, barely visible in the moonlight, something or someone is lying across the path.

Marshalling all her nerve, Kate steps forward. It is the body of a thin, tall man. He is not moving. Where his hair had been is a glistening dark mass. She gasps, drawing a hand to her mouth and steps back, her heels striking something solid and soft.

Turning quickly she recognizes the small body of a girl her own age, sprawled face down in the burdock and wild mustard. Nearby lies the body of her mother, her chemise draped loosely over her head.

Choking down the rising panic, Kate turns and runs to the river. Skidding down clay banks, tears streaming, sobs catching in her throat, she fights off the image of the girl's sprawling corpse. Into the canoe, flailing across the river, she sprints straight to her mother's bed.

"Mam! Wake up!" she hisses "We've got to get out of here."

Pulled from sleep, Phoebe blinks twice and then stares: "What's wrong?"

"Mam we've got to get out of here.! Something awful's happened, the Kanes are all dead!"

A look of panic crosses her face, then she steadies: "Take Robert, Ephraim and the baby, and head to the big oak. I'll take Phoebe and meet you. Now go!"

"John! Abel!" she shouts to the loft, "Drive the cows and the hogs into the woods and meet us at the big oak!"

In a minute the house is empty and Kate, clutching baby Will to her chest and Robert and Ephraim right behind, is scrambling over the newly planted corn and beans.

Phoebe, a red and blue quilt wrapped around her shoulders and young Phoebe in tow, arrives, followed by John. She is about to ask after Abel when a high-pitched yell comes from the homestead.

Looking back through the gloom towards the house, Phoebe can see a reddish glow that quickly bursts into flame. There are forms moving in and out of the house.

Flames lick around the doorframe and the orange glow reaches deep into the forest.

Behind a fallen tree, Phoebe tastes tears while she nurses William.

Early in the morning a light rain begins to fall, the grey clouds smudging the dawn light that leads them, wet and cold, out of the woods. Although the rain has stopped, thick clouds hang low between the mountains. The air is heavy with the damp, sooty smell of charred timber. The house they built—their refuge, their pride—is completely gone, save for the foundation and the stone chimney from which a wisp of smoke still rises in the still morning air.

The stable, smokehouse and husking pen are just piles of steaming charcoal. The only building still standing is the privy. Two partially butchered hogs, already home to a swarm of blow flies, lie in the yard beside the hickory harrow. Phoebe's large, silvered looking glass, that survived two generations with her family in Virginia, lies shattered beside a large iron pot. "Both too cumbersome to plunder, I reckon," says John to no-one in particular.

Staring at the mirror, Phoebe's lips tremble. Squeezing her eyes shut she stands motionless for a few seconds, commanding the tears to stop, then taking a deep breath, wipes her sleeve across her eyes and calls to Kate.

"I expect there's still some good corn in the bottom of the husking pen, it should be well parched There's a basket of maple sugar in the root cellar."

'Phoebe, you see if you can't find any of our beasts in the bush. Robert, Ephraim, find out if they left us any hens, they'll be looking for a place to lay and we can use the eggs."

"What's happened to Abel, mother?" Kate asks as the two boys move away. Do you think he might have gone to the Mitchell's? Or do you think he's ..."

"Now Kate. Abel's a man, he can take care of himself. I'm near certain he'll be along shortly." Phoebe turns away to stare at the ruins.

ℭℬ

"they generally die…though they struggle with all the violence of hope and despair."
—Freegift Patchin

As Phoebe is mixing eggs and cornmeal, Abel is wondering if he will ever see his family again.

Struggling under a bulging pack, hands tied with rawhide, he is tethered from the neck behind a painted warrior. Staggering under the weight he is being dragged and prodded through the woods with the small Iroquois war party that swept through Cushetunk the previous night.

Abel had just driven the cows into the bush when he was confronted by two warriors: one his face painted half-red, half-black wearing a brocade waistcoat, the other with a silk scarf over his breechcloth.

Abel turned to flee but before he could take a step, the butt of a rounded war club crashed a glancing blow on the back of his skull and he dropped to his knees.

Through the threatening, pounding darkness he struggled to rise, to avoid the killing blow that would surely be followed by the cutting and lifting of his scalp.

But to his surprise it never came and he felt a rush of relief when he was dragged to his feet and his hands bound behind him while his captors argued. Although he understood not a word, he knew what the reprieve meant. Iroquois families adopted prisoners to replace sons lost in battle.

The party's pace is brutal. Abel's feet are torn, his head aches.

He is struggling to find some slack in the rawhide tether when the whole party halts, alert to the sound of approaching horses.

Dragging Abel by the neck they turn to confront a mixed party of whites and natives including his father's good friend Joseph Ross and a local Delaware chief.

His captors, their muskets cocked and clubs poised, stand stock-still, staring defiantly at the mounted party while the grey-haired chief speaks. The response, delivered solemnly by the Iroquois war chief, leaves no doubt they plan to keep their captive.

The discussion, growing louder and more animated, continues for more than an hour.

Finally the talking ends and Abel can see his original captors—brocade and silk scarf—scowling displeasure at what's been decided. His heart soars.

Ross approaches, leans close and whispers: "They're Oneidas, Abel and I'll hazard they were put up to this raid by Tyler and the Peenpack rabble. We've tried everything, including ransom offers and threats. They don't want the first and they don't believe the second but we've made a bargain of sorts. They'll give you up as prisoner…but only after you run the gauntlet."

Abel feels a fist clench in his stomach and he can only stare at Ross with widening eyes.

"Lad, I'm truly sorry but it's the best I could do. We could stand and fight but you'd be first to die. You know that."

Abel is stunned. Men do survive the Indian gauntlet, but not without being maimed or injured.

Warriors are strung out in two parallel lines about 40 feet in length and six feet apart. Armed with war clubs and stout boughs, they position themselves so they can easily swing their weapons.

Abel's goal is to run the gauntlet between the two lines as swiftly as he can, evading the intended blows. Any misstep or tumble will bring a rain of deadly blows.

His bonds are released and to his surprise he is handed a bowl of hominy. While he eats, one of his captors rubs a soothing mix of beeswax and bearfat into his raw feet.

Around him warriors whoop and swing their clubs so that they sing and whiz.

Drawing to his feet Abel deliberately looks away. Run, he reasons, as hard as he can and pray for deliverance.

Slowly rocking from his forward left foot to his rear right one, Abel stares at the middle ground between the two lines, clenching and unclenching his hands, drawing great deliberate draughts of air.

Run! His heart screams and he launches himself down the gauntlet.

The first blow comes from a husky young warrior wielding a bough like a broadsword. His clumsy, ill-timed swing at Abel's head is easily avoided but the downstroke glances off his shoulder.

The arm dies then instantly screams back to life.

The pain, like a white-hot poker, drives him to even greater speed. Several times Abel feels the lethal breeze of near-misses and the damaging bite of near-hits as he gallops madly down the gauntlet, a howling, whirling corridor of hell. Careening from one crunching blow to the next, aware only of a swirling mass of bared teeth, dark eyes and shrieking mouths. In what remains of his rational mind he is beginning to think he might just survive…when a fearsome maple warclub—a carved hand holding a ball—crashes into his ribs.

The air leaves his body and is replaced with howling agony. His brain blacks and the last thing he remembers is a storming swarm of blows. There is darkness and blessed silence.

A fiery, burning taste on his tongue summons Abel up from the deep well into which he has fallen. The taste become rum, the eyes flutter open and see Captain Ross, a silver flask in his hand. The Indians are gone. There is a sharp, searing pain when he breathes.

"Providence is with you Abel," Ross says. "You stumbled under that warclub but you staggered on and made it clear. Near as I can tell nothing's broken. You've a couple of ribs that are likely cracked, some colossal bruises and you're missing a few bits of flesh here and there but, by and large, you're intact."

☙

"A Tory is a thing whose head is in England, its body in America and its neck ought to be stretched..."
—definition of Loyalist

"Must I die a second time?"
—Joseph Wilson

In the days following the raid, John uses the surviving timber to rig a lean-to for the family. Abel, his ribs bound with strips of linen, is in no shape to help. Captain Ross brings blankets and urges Phoebe to move the family back into the highlands away from the river.

The corn meal nearly gone, John takes a sack of seed grain and paddles downriver where in return for a small portion of their flour, settlers have their grain ground.

The miller, however, keeps almost half. When John protests, he sneers and says he'll keep as much Tory grain as he damn'd well pleases.

By noon John is on the return trip, paddling steadily against the lazy Delaware current. He has just come into a broad sweep known as Big Eddy when he hears his name.

Standing on Pennsylvania shore, with two other dismounted riders, is a neighbour, Joe Thomas, smiling and beckoning to him.

"John, John Land, c'mon ashore," he says in a friendly tone.

"I guess I'll just stay right here, Joe. I've some grist I should fetch back to Cushetunk.

"John," Thomas calls across the water, "Is it true Abel got snatched by Indians? Is he well? Put in and tell us about it. Yer needn't fear, we're all scared silly of the savages. Need to help each other. We got some sot weed, c'mon in for a smoke. We'll talk."

Remembering better times and fancying a pipe, John pulls in to the rocky shallows. Beaching the canoe, he stows his paddle, steps out and extends a hand to Thomas.

Thomas, cocks his arm as if to grasp it, then drawing his hand into a fist, draws back and drives it deep into John's stomach, doubling him over.

Immediately two other men are on his arms dragging him roughly to his feet and binding his hands behind him with a strip of hide.

From behind a rock Bezaleel Tyler steps out. "You Lands are all stupid."

Struggling to regain his breath John gasps: "What deceit is this? Why are you doing this?"

"Because you're a government man, a Tory traitor. We're at war and you're the enemy."

John looks fiercely at Tyler, then at Thomas, "You were my friend. You ate at our table."

"Afore I saw your true colours," Thomas spits back. "How many helpless folk have you murdered?"

"I haven't killed anyone you idiot," John says with a flush of anger.

Drawing a pistol, Thomas cocks the hammer and stabs John's chest. "I'd shoot yer for naught if it was up to me."

"No, no, you don't want to do that," says Tyler smiling again, "what we've got in mind is something a bit slower.

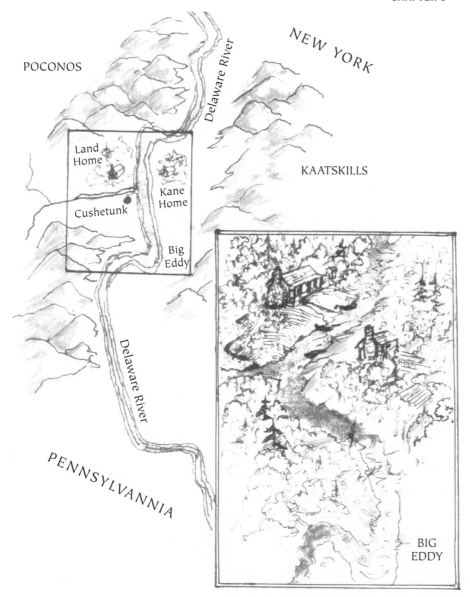

Turning to his horse he draws a length of bristly rope and fashions a noose. "Now John Land, I'm going to ask you again. How many innocents have you slaughtered?"

John looks wildly at the rope and then at Tyler, "I-I-I... haven't done harm to anyone," he protests. "I swear I've not gone to the Royal Standard, I've never spoken ill of the Congress. You know I've always dealt straight and fair."

"Your father's a Tory scoundrel and I say the acorn don't fall far from the oak. Speaking of which, that one yonder looks serviceable enough, don't you think? Take him lads."

Sliding the noose over John's head, Tyler turns and with the rest of the rope slung over his shoulder begins to walk towards the nearby oak. He plays the rope out until he is several paces ahead and then grasping the end and setting his shoulder forward, jerks John along behind him.

Standing under the tree Tyler throws the heavy rope over the lowest bough and steps up so he is nose-to-nose with John. "Once more, own up your treachery? Tell us the truth and I promise I won't hang you."

John, pale and trembling at the knees, feels tears welling up in his eyes, feels bowels threatening to give way.

"Cap'n Tyler," he pleads, "I've done you no harm, why are you using me so cruelly?"

"Because you're a Tory, John Land, just like your father, the magistrate. You Lands are royal arse-lickers. You took that prime land along the river and left the likes of Tylers to farm rocks on the hillside. I reckon that's what this war is all about—getting rid of blood suckers like you.

You ready for a glimpse of eternity? Bowse that line a tug, you two, put your shoulders into it."

At that moment, John Land experiences two simultaneous sensations: One, a terrifying constriction of his windpipe, the other, the realization his feet are being lifted off the ground.

Eyes bulging, mouth agape around a swollen, purpling tongue, John is then only aware of one thing: a rapid dimming of light and sensation as his brain loses oxygen.

Then his feet slam the ground with a thump and he crumples, coughing and gagging. His neck feels as if someone has burned a deep ring around it and his temple throbs with a pain that begins deep inside his head. "Dear God," he thinks, "my heart's going to burst." Slowly as his vision begins to clear, the fist that clenched his guts begins to ease and he hears Tyler's voice.

"Did the altitude improve your memory? Are you ready to tell us the truth now? How many plantations have you burned? How many women ravished? How many babies scolped, you bastard?"

His system still in shock, John can only croak: "None, I've hurt no-one."

"Craven villain!" Tyler hisses, "give him another taste of the cords boys. By God he'll cry cockles before we're done."

Once more the heavy brown rope sings over the bough, once more the rag doll figure is hauled by the neck until its feet are kicking free above the ground.

Then Joe Thomas, a smallish man speaks, "How about you tug on the line a spell, Zeel; this Tory's getting to be a dead weight and I'm about clawed out, 'sides, he looks scragged to me."

"Ah Thomas, you are a milksop sissy. This be righteous work and you have the cause of liberty to strengthen your arm."

"Maybe so Zeel but lessn you add yours I'm going to let him down."

John, who has been twitching and making strange "clacking" noises in his throat, is suddenly still and silent.

"There now, he's done," says Thomas, "and so am I," as lets loose the rope spilling John unto the ground like a sack of old clothes.

"Fetch a bucket of water, Conklin, young Mr. Land appears in need of restoration."

Tyler loosens the noose and throws the water into John's purple face. Nothing happens.

"Tip a little grog into his gob, Thomas, but not too much. I'd hate to waste good rum on a dead Tory."

The raw spirit dribbling from his mouth connects somewhere. John manages a faint cough followed by a long, laboured wheeze as he once more draws air deep into his lungs.

Unable to move, aware that he has teetered on the verge of eternal blackness, John knows he will not survive another session. He tries to speak but his throat is so swollen and torn that all that emerges is a faint, bubbling grunt.

"C'mon lads, off yer fundaments," grunts Tyler, "one more trip and we'll be rid of this vile sack of guts. Haul him up!"

But neither Thomas or Conklin, who are sitting on the ground, move.

"Zeel," says Thomas, "Land is near to perished now. If you want him finished off yer going to do it yourself 'cause we're plain tucked up."

Tyler's eyes flash for a moment as he stares at Thomas, then shrugs and turns toward the prone figure on the ground.

"You're a sorry mess John Land but we're not going to end your misery just yet, I guess. There's a snug gaol over in New Jersey built by old Judge Green where they lodge traitors. I warrant you'll fit right in."

February, 1778

☙

"I am every day at straits for the bare necessities of life..."
—Joshua Hett Smith

They cut off John Hancock's hand yesterday.

The repair crew had cried "huzzah" and an extra gill of rum all round when a young jack tar shinnied up the underside of the bowsprit and, with a cutlass, neatly lopped off the figurehead's right hand.

Robert Land had cheered as loudly as any of the joiners and carpenters on board when the pine hand dropped to the icy East River.

The 34-gun HANCOCK, a frigate bearing the name and effigy of the first—and most prominent—signatory of the Declaration of Independence, had a brief but glorious career in the Rebel Navy, before being captured off New England by a British squadron.

Towed to the King's Shipyard in New York for repair and refit, the ship was recommissioned HMS IRIS, whereupon the new captain immediately ordered removal of the figurehead's right hand, the hand Hancock used to sign the momentous document.

The act, an insult and show of British disdain for the Rebels, was also a morale booster for dock workers living and working under difficult wartime conditions.

Land and his son Abel have fled to the city of New York because Cushetunk has become a dangerous place for Loyalists. After defying the local committee of safety, his farm had been burned, Abel captured by Indians and John kidnapped, and possibly killed, by Rebels. Neighbours have warned the magistrate that Captain Mush has sworn an oath to destroy him.

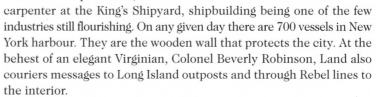

To escape from the Delaware corridor, Phoebe has moved her family a day's journey into the nearby highlands. The entire family has become outcasts.

In New York Abel's a navvy in the British Ordnance Department, his father's a carpenter at the King's Shipyard, shipbuilding being one of the few industries still flourishing. On any given day there are 700 vessels in New York harbour. They are the wooden wall that protects the city. At the behest of an elegant Virginian, Colonel Beverly Robinson, Land also couriers messages to Long Island outposts and through Rebel lines to the interior.

New York is a grim, feverish place, no longer the prosperous and cosmopolitan port he'd married Phoebe in 20 years earlier. Even their wedding church, the graceful Trinity on Broadway, is gone, destroyed in the fire that consumed more than 1,000 buildings just days after the British occupation began in 1776.

The King's forces, having abandoned Boston, have all their eggs in one basket—New York. Its great harbour maintains the supply lifeline with Britain but it is only a foothold fortress in an otherwise hostile landscape.

Military occupation—briefly first by Washington's army, then by the British, has diminished the former Dutch colonial capital. The city occupies only the southern tip of New York Island—something less than a square mile. Most of Manhattan is still given over to substantial farms and country estates—Greenwich, Bloomingdale and Harlem are but remote rural hamlets. The Bouwerie is exactly what it means in Dutch—a farm. New York maintains a Dutch flavour with gabled houses and cobbled streets with gutters down the centre. The main road, Broadway, runs north from Fort George past elegant residences, stately churches, stores and taverns.

The population, now approaching 30,000, is composed largely of three distinct groups: British troops, "Geldsoldaten"—German mercenaries—and Loyalist refugees who pour in daily from all over the colonies. Many, including formerly well to-do merchants and artisans, survive on charity. There are several thousand Rebel prisoners wretchedly lodged in warehouses, churches and in stinking prison hulks anchored in the harbour. The ships are death traps and kill more Rebels than British arms.

Fed entirely from Britain, New York is rife with shortages, want and privation.

Supply, which depends on Atlantic weather, is precarious and what victuals do arrive are frequently unfit to eat. Salt pork, a staple of most diets, is poorly cured and often riddled with worms.

Hunger for the rich means starvation for the poor. Firewood for cooking and heating is scant and very expensive. Nearly every tree in the city, including ornamentals, has been cut. Housing, in the wake of the great fire and the huge refugee influx, is scarce. A good portion of the population, including the Lands, live in the squalor of Canvas Town, a sprawl of tents and shanties that has been thrown up over the charred site of the great fire. The city's main water supply—fresh water pond—is polluted. The stink of the city—the garbage, the open sewers, the night soil thick in the streets—is Land's strongest first impression.

There is also a sense of unease in the air for the whole complexion of the war has changed.

General John Burgoyne's expedition to invade the colony of New York from Canada was a disaster, ending with the surrender of nearly 8,000 Crown troops at Saratoga. A related foray against Fort Stanwix in the Mohawk Valley also failed. The third part of the equation, a Northern movement by Sir Henry Clinton from New York City, foundered for want of leadership. The intended masterstroke of dividing the colonies and breaking the back of the revolt has come to naught.

And to deepen the mood of pessimism, Britain's traditional enemy, France, has also declared war on Britain. From Philadelphia, captured just months before by the British, come rumors the largest city in the colonies is to be abandoned.

In a matter of a year chances of a swift British victory have evaporated. Loyalist refugees like Land begin to confront something previously unthinkable: a Rebel victory and the prospect of never going home.

In the fall of 1778 Land receives the following letter carried by an Upper Delaware neighbour.

My Dear Robert:

I hope when you receive these few lines they may find you in good health. We are much distressed at our circumstances. We have removed to Beach Lake & have a roof overhead but not the means to feed ourselves. The soil is stony & supports little. The cow we were forced to sell receiving but little in return—only two sacks of flour. We are Obliged to Live but very Short. Were it not for the Charity of Captain Ross we must certainly perish. We are badly used by the neighbours with insults and unkind words. We have no word from John, I pray he lives still. Kate is considerable help to me and minds the baby, Phoebe tends the boys. My Dearest Robert please send relief by the first safe hand. May God bless and protect you is the constant prayer of

your affectionate wife.
Phoebe

PS The childers kind love to you

CHAPTER 8

℃ℨ

"Parricides, wretches, deluded mortals!"
—George Washington

At nights in the dockside tap-rooms that flourish along the East River, Land nurses tankards of dark West Indies rum—one of the few things still cheap and plentiful in the city—and wonders how his prospects could have fallen so low.

"Seventeen years I laboured on the Upper Delaware," he tells a table of co-workers. "When we arrived, with two babies and another on the way, the bush was so thick you were lost fifty feet from the river

I chopped and hauled for thirty-seven days to clear three acres of that bottom land. Built a bark hut for Phoebe and the little ones.

Lived through the first year on samp and potatoes. The winter was punishing but next spring I got corn and beans in the ground. God granted us a bountiful harvest.

Each spring the river filled with shad—so plentiful they could be drawn by the bucket—as well as eels, trout and flatfish. The smokehouse was never empty. The larder was always full.

The forests teemed with game—a rare day there wasn't venison or partridge for the table. And if you had time there was plenty of peltry to be had including fox and beaver.

I built a log house the second year, cleared another three acres and turned a few sticks of furniture. Phoebe made potash pearl-ash from the timber we burned and sold it, sixpence a bushel. Had a competency of worldly goods.

Neighbours all helped one another. Least they did until those Boston Rebels stirred things up and some of our idle and envious neighbours got the notion we'd stolen something that belonged to them.

The Lands have always worked hard and I won't abide anyone who speaks otherwise. These rogues were talking treason, men have hanged for less.

Not once, not even for a moment, have I wavered. I could have taken the oath and hung back like some but I did what I believed was right. I went with Brant and done things I'd sooner forget. I've recruited all through the Delaware for Brant and Butler, I've carried dispatches to Fort Niagara and Montreal. Lived on Indian potatoes, wild onions and salt, and cinched in my gut with a belt.

And what have I gained for my trouble? My eldest son in a Rebel gaol, my family burned out, my property forfeit and my own life at hazard. You tell me, have I paid the price of loyalty?

All around me I see British fops, loathe to lead their men into battle for fear they'll miss the opening of the theatre season. They care more for their hounds than they do for our homes and families.

New York City is full of the best troops in the world but it all comes to naught for want of leadership at the top.

General George makes a mockery of King George. We, who live here, have burned our bridges. It is us, and our children, who will pay because the British tire of their colonial adventure.

Our generals, while they have stomachs to be sure, have no stomach for war. I fear betrayal more than I fear Rebel guns."

March, 1779

ↂ

"One of the greatest villains in these parts…"
—John Schott

"I am obliged to say more than the truth to encourage them to come out."
—Charles Smith

Ice thumps the jolly boat. The oarsmen slowly pull it across the Hudson. Although a thin sun hangs above the horizon, Land and his companions pull blanket coats tight and sink below the gunnels to escape the bitter north wind that sweeps the vast river.

After a year in New York, Land is on his way to the frontier again, traveling in a party of three former Wyoming settlers.

Thomas Hill and Peter Mabee are sullen, bitter men, hardened by the circumstance of war. Edward Hicks, under arms since he was 16, carries mail from families separated by the war. Their destination is the Crown's Lake Ontario stronghold, Fort Niagara. In an oilskin wallet Land carries despatches to Butler and Brant.

The boat grinds ashore against the built-up ice on the Jersey side, a tar securing it long enough for the four men to scramble ashore with packs and muskets. It then slides back to the grey water, comes about and heads back to the island that is New York.

Each man shoulders a provision pack with snow shoes lashed to the outside and slings a musket, barrel down, over his right shoulder. They'll spend the night within British lines but tomorrow will strike across rebel New Jersey and make for the Upper Delaware.

Much has occurred in the year since Land came to the provincial capital. England's perennial enemy, France has weighed into the war on the Rebel side, prompting great nervousness in New York. Almost daily there are rumours the French fleet, which hovered nearby the previous summer, is about to return and spearhead an invasion of New York. In June the British, in a major reversal, were forced to evacuate Philadelphia after holding it only nine months. The war that began with predictions of a rout is now anything but.

And yet British arms have found considerable success on the frontiers. Loyalist units and Indian allies are waging a viciously effective guerrilla war that has devastated isolated communities like Wyoming and Cherry Valley and denied the Continental Army desperately needed supplies of wheat.

Land and his small party hopes to swing across Rebel New Jersey, moving between safe Loyalist houses until they reach the Upper Delaware. From there, after collecting recruits for the Indian Department, he plans to take his family to Fort Niagara.

A week after leaving New York they are on the Delaware, near Minisink. Winter still has a firm grip on the region—the river has a solid ice cover and a man without snowshoes will sink to his waist in the accumulated snow.

Recruiting for the Crown requires a mixture of enticement and appeal to duty, with a measure of threat thrown in.

"The government will remember its friends when this rebellion's been put down," Land tells the poor tenant farmers, "and the ring leaders will hang.

It's your duty to serve the King," he says, "more so now the Boston levellers have this unholy covenant with France."

The latter goes down well with many on the frontier who, like Land, fought the French a generation earlier over much of the same ground.

"And besides, the next time Brant or Butler comes down the Delaware we wouldn't want them to harm any friend of government simply because he hadn't proclaimed his loyalty loud enough, now would we?"

It's tough going though. The settlers, while sympathetic to the Crown, fear their homes will be seized or destroyed by the Rebels if they leave. Land like all recruiters in all wars, is obliged to say more than the truth.

And then there is the constant risk of informers. One can never be certain the smiling, welcoming face isn't really the mask of a spy who reports to the Rebel militia in Minisink.

After a day of showshoeing between the cabins of former neighbours, the recruiting party has lodged in a safe house on the New York side of the Delaware a day's travel below Cushetunk. The owner having just tabled supper, answers a knock on the door to reveal a small, dark man. Land, sitting at the end of the table, leaps from his chair to grab for his musket. The man ducks back out the door and runs off.

"I know who he is," Land says, "name's Ventail, one of those weasels who dragged me afore the committee. I'll wager he's on his way right now to call out the militia."

After a sleepless night they're gone well before first light. For two days they scrabble over the mountains doubling back on the trail, splitting up and reforming. Land spends an hour on a patch of high ground watching the trail they've just covered as it spreads out below him. The only things moving are the ravens.

On the afternoon of the third day they are descending to the river, only a few miles from Cushetunk, when Land hears the dogs. The first few, faint barks quickly became louder and faster.

Hill and Mabee break for high ground. Land and the lad Hicks desperately make for the river but are soon overtaken and backed up against a rock face by three snarling bull mastiffs. Land manages to fit the bayonet on his musket and is attempting to fend off the lead dog when a voice calls out: "I wouldn't do that Cap'n Land, you might get one but the other two'll chew your hide off. Besides, you hurt one of my dogs and I'll shoot you. Same goes for you lad."

Land turns to a tall, skinny man now flanked by four other panting militiamen, regards him briefly and drops the flintlock.

The officer, a lieutenant named Decker, ropes the dogs and then collects the packs and hunting bags of his captives.

By the time the patrol gets its prisoners back to the small Minisink garrison, Decker, who reads but little, has guessed, from the elaborate wax seals on some of the documents that they are of considerable importance.

The garrison captain, a shoemaker in civilian life, is delighted when he sees the signature of Henry Clinton across the bottom of letters to Brant and Butler.

He isn't sure what they actually say but he knows the two carrying them—the notorious Land and the stripling Hicks will pay dearly for transporting them.

Within days a court martial has been assembled and the pair officially charged with spying and carrying intelligence to the enemy. Land's trial begins on a cold, grey morning. In a Minisink tavern, heavy with the smell of rum and tobacco, four plank tables are fitted together to accommodate the two majors, six captains and four junior officers who make up the court martial.

Typically they are a mix of Continental officers—Spencer's Regiment, Armand's Partisans and the locally raised German Regiment, their uniforms a mix of dull browns and greens.

Although it's still winter outside, the landlord will furnish only the most meagre fire and it is miserably cold in the room. Several of the officers have heavy great coats slung over their shoulders.

Land, wearing his blanket coat and a brace of leg irons shuffles into the tavern between two ragged soldiers to stand in front of the assembled officers.

Every eye is trained on this man. They know who he is. One of Brant's Volunteers—*Cherry Valley!* The word traitor is on every lip—*Wyoming!* He stands before the court president, a stout, florid-faced lieutenant-colonel with cold, hard eyes while the charge is read.

"Prisoner Robert Land, citizen of the Commonwealth of Pennsylvania, under the authority granted this court martial by the Congress of the United States you are charged with being a spy and carrying intelligence to the enemy. How do you plead?"

Land narrows his eyes and takes the measure of the men facing him.

"You have no jurisdiction in this matter," he begins, "I am a civilian and not subject to a military court."

"How do you plead!" thunders the president fixing Land with a fierce gaze.

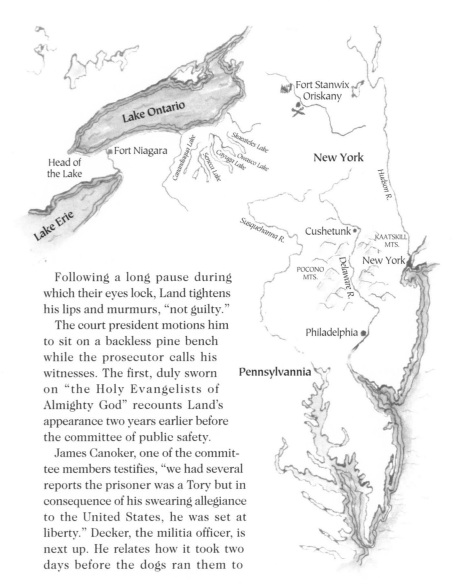

Following a long pause during which their eyes lock, Land tightens his lips and murmurs, "not guilty."

The court president motions him to sit on a backless pine bench while the prosecutor calls his witnesses. The first, duly sworn on "the Holy Evangelists of Almighty God" recounts Land's appearance two years earlier before the committee of public safety.

James Canoker, one of the committee members testifies, "we had several reports the prisoner was a Tory but in consequence of his swearing allegiance to the United States, he was set at liberty." Decker, the militia officer, is next up. He relates how it took two days before the dogs ran them to ground, two had escaped but Land and Hicks had letters and despatches with them.

Even as a backwoods magistrate, Land knows the evidence does not support a charge of treason . Court Martials are for soldiers. In the eyes of the law he is a civilian. At worst he should be held as a prisoner of war. He was simply planning to collect his family and take them to Fort Niagara, a common enough occurrence during the war. Without proof they can't convict and without a conviction they'll have to let him go, probably send him on his way as good riddance with warnings not to come back. With that assurance he spends the rest of the day barely noticing the proceedings.

The second day however, the complexion of the trial changes dramatically when the prosecutor calls his last witness.

It's been snowing most of the day—heavy, late-season snow that seems to fall in clumps—and the plank floors are puddled with melt-water. The fire in the grate smokes and steams but gives little in the way of heat.

The prosecutor and judge advocate, a small, wiry man with bad teeth and watery blue eyes, leaves the makeshift court for a few minutes and then returns holding open the slab-sided door.

Still wearing the same mocking grin, Bezaleel Tyler strides into the courtroom, beats the snow from his felt hat and takes the bible from the clerk.

In a grating, high-pitched voice he repeats the oath, his gaze never wavering from Land.

"You are a scout for the Continentals, Captain Tyler?" the prosecutor asks. "How long have you known the prisoner?"

"Since I was a green stick. The Lands lived downriver, picked out a spread of prime bottom land. He fancied himself a magistrate. Told anyone who'd listen that he would never take up arms against the King and those that did should be hanged. Then just to show what a deceitful wretch he is, under oath—this magistrate—swears an oath of allegiance."

And so it goes. Tyler, never taking his eyes off Land. Never changing the half-smirk, he gives the court martial exactly the sort of evidence it seeks—Land has been seen with Brant, has recruited for the King, has incited the Indians with promises of gifts and rum. "There's blood on his hands, and both his sons too," Tyler tells the court martial. "Even his wife admitted he was carrying messages to those butchers at Niagara. There's orphans and widows up and down the Delaware thanks to this man."

Land feels as if the earth has opened up and swallowed him, like he's been slammed in the guts by the butt-end of a log. Tyler, his eyes gleaming like a madman, continues to spin his fabric of half-truth and innuendo. In the end Land is left powerless and exhausted. He has no witnesses to call. And for all the righteousness in his heart he can hardly deny the fact that he was apprehended carrying dispatches for Fort Niagara. The witnesses have cast his character and credibility in the worst possible light.

Slowly, fighting the clenched fist his stomach has become, he rises. The leg-irons clank and scrape, despite the near-freezing temperatures in the room, there is a ridge of sweat on his brow.

"You have heard today that I am the product of privilege," he says with a weary sigh, "that my only motivation was gain, that I willingly sacrificed the lives of my countrymen to uphold that privilege.

Well I ask you,"—thrusting forth his hands, palms up—"do these look like privileged hands. You can see for yourself they are cracked and scarred, the mark of honest labour, without which I have won nothing in this life. I have sought only to uphold the legal government, indeed as I am sworn to do as a magistrate. For that I am cast as spawn of the devil. My property is forfeit, my family has been abused and beaten. We are outcasts, no longer welcome in the country of our birth. For that I have sought to remove them to Canada, but having been apprehended in the process I stand before you accused of treason. Why? Because I seek to protect my family? Because I carried sealed despatches to Niagara? Yes, I have counselled with Brant and the savages but not, as you have been told, to incite them to plunder and destroy the frontiers. Rather it has been to spare all the inhabitants save those in arms against us.

It is true I have no-one to testify for me, but as God is my witness gentlemen, I am no traitor for I have betrayed nothing. I have betrayed no-one."

Land slowly sinks down to the bench and watches the president scratch some notes. Although the snow has stopped it is colder than ever in the tavern. Frost is beginning to shroud the windows. A soldier rakes the ashes and throws on another green log.

The prosecutor, rubbing the stubble on his chin, stands and walks to the middle of the room.

"This man, for all his protestations of innocence, is an enemy of the Unites States. He has turned his back on friends and neighbours and enlisted in the cause of the tyrant, King George. By his wanton goading of the savage he has caused the death of untold innocents. Yet he has the gall to stand before you and speak of his honour as a magistrate. I submit this court martial offer Robert Land no more than his due—a generous share of Continental hemp."

The verdict is not long coming. The president, Lt. Col. Ebeneazer Lindsley, pronounces it in a voice as dry as dust:

"This court considering the case of the prisoner, the evidence against him and his defence, is unanimously of the opinion that he is guilty of the charges exhibited against him and do therefore sentence him to suffer death."

Lowering the paper Lindsley looks briefly at Land before seizing a quill to sign it.

Led from the courtroom past a small knot of onlookers, Land looks desperately for a friendly face. Instead all he finds is the triumphant, mocking smile of Bezaleel Tyler. "I guess we're done with you now, Judge Land."

That night in a dark corner of the tavern stable, Land, still wearing his leg irons, sits bent-over on a wooden bench, his head cradled in his hands. The death sentence? It hardly seems possible. At worst he expected to be sent to the Simsbury Mine in Connecticut. Even the most zealous of the Rebel courts generally stopped short of hanging.

He sits all night on that bench until an hour before dawn when a fitful, feverish sleep haunted by Tyler's mocking grin steals over him.

At noon the next day the guard relays the news the same court martial has found Hicks guilty of spying but stopped short of invoking the death sentence—he's going to Simsbury until the war is over.

That night while an army courier is making his way to headquarters with transcripts of both court martials, Edward Hicks is taking matters into his own hands.

Terrified by tales he's heard of Simsbury—that time in the old mine shaft is worse than a death sentence—Hicks bolts at the first chance.

Freed of his shackles to walk to a transport cart he elbows one guard out of the way and makes a desperate dash for the woods. He can hear the excited yells, the sharp clicks as they cock their muskets, the rolling booms and the sound of something whizzing past his ear. Then he's in the woods and gone.

Patrols are out all night—they even unleash Decker's mastiffs—but there's no sign of Hicks.

As a consequence, Land is kept shackled around the clock and the guards, who are constantly with him, make grim jokes about having to hang him twice to make up for Hicks. One of his captors though, an old Pole in Armand's Corps, brings Land a small knife and chunks of basswood which he whittles into a series of small animal figures. First a bear, then a horse, then a fish, then a cat and so on—each one dated and bearing the initials RL. The Pole has agreed to forward them upriver to Cushetunk in hopes they'll find their way to his family.

But the day before he is due to be hanged there is an uproar in the garrison guard room. A courier who has ridden all night brings a letter to the garrison commander from Washington's aide-de-camp. "By the articles of war," it reads, "Robert Land as an inhabitant of one of the states, is not subject to military jurisdiction. You will therefore have him delivered up to the civil authority. He can be sent to Easton and there consigned over to the civil magistrate. Care should be taken that he does not escape."

May, 1779

℃

"These people before these unhappy disputes lived in ease and affluence but are now obliged to wash and sew for bread."
—Nicholas Cresswell

"The want of every necessity of life and the continual insults of the Rebels obliged her to leave the Province of New York."
—Abigail Hare petition

New York is a city in chaos. The clean and graceful seaport Phoebe remembers from a quarter of a century earlier has become a swarming hive, rife with squalor and crime. Where there were groves of mature trees there are now only ugly stumps. Last winter the wood shortage was severe—the rivers never froze and teamsters were unable to sled over any firewood. As a result nearly every fruit, ornamental and shade tree in the city fell to the axe for fuel.

Civilian refugees continue to pour into a city already dangerously swollen by nearly 30,000 soldiers. Every day another load of Rebel prisoners arrives to be stuffed into confiscated churches or prison hulks in the river where they die almost as fast as they arrive. Many other churches have been taken over for hospitals. Food and shelter are difficult to secure and outlandishly expensive. The price of bread has increased fivefold since the war began, rent for private quarters, fourfold. Hundreds of refugee families are still living under canvas strung over the charred remnants of the great fire. Is it any wonder there are ragged, wretched beggars on nearly every street corner?

It is four days since Phoebe and her five children arrived in the colonial capital as part of a small convoy of New York and Pennsylvania Loyalists. It had taken 10 days to walk from the Delaware travelling with only the clothes on their backs and sustained by a small amount of corn meal and some withered onions. William, only two, had to be carried, the load shared between the two oldest girls, Phoebe and Kate. On some nights they had been able to shelter in barns but twice it had rained while they slept in the open. Fortunately the weather was mild. The group of four families was escorted under a Rebel flag as far as New Jersey and then left to cross into British lines and make their way to New York. Phoebe had hoped to find Abel in the city but the clerk at the Ordnance Board said he was with the army building fortifications on Long Island.

Phoebe's initial exhilaration on reaching the British stronghold quickly passes with the realization families of Loyalists are not particularly welcome. The military command administering New York views women and children as baggage, unproductive consumers of valuable rations.

To survive, they must be prepared to take care of themselves.

Before she left the Delaware, Phoebe and Kate climbed high into the hills flanking Big Eddy with a gunny sack of family heirlooms that

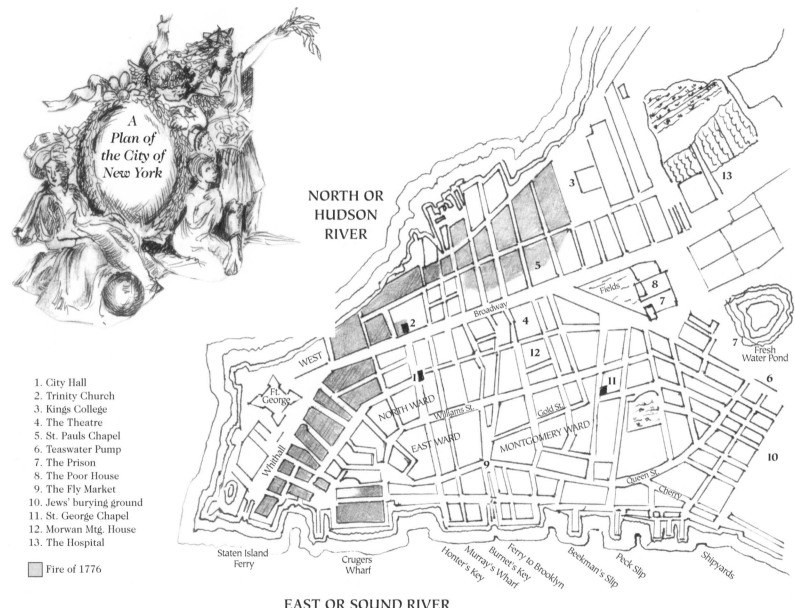

A
Plan of
the City of
New York

NORTH OR
HUDSON
RIVER

1. City Hall
2. Trinity Church
3. Kings College
4. The Theatre
5. St. Pauls Chapel
6. Teaswater Pump
7. The Prison
8. The Poor House
9. The Fly Market
10. Jews' burying ground
11. St. George Chapel
12. Morwan Mtg. House
13. The Hospital

Fire of 1776

Fields

Fresh
Water Pond

WEST

Ft.
George

Broadway

Williams St.

Gold St.

Whithall

NORTH WARD

EAST WARD

MONTGOMERY WARD

Queen St.

Cherry

Staten Island
Ferry

Crugers
Wharf

Honter's Key

Murray's Wharf

Burnet's Key

Ferry to Brooklyn

Beekman's Slip

Peck Slip

Shipyards

EAST OR SOUND RIVER

Robert had buried behind their house when he left to join Brant. On a rock face so sheer they had been afraid to look down, they had inched their way upward until they found the cleft Robert had discovered years before. In a hollow just big enough to admit one person they had cached the sack and covered it with brush and rocks.

With her to New York Phoebe has brought two silver brooches, a pair of silver knee buckles, an elegantly worked snuffbox, three silver spoons, five Spanish dollars and her gold wedding band. One of the brooches she had given as security for the single room they'd taken in a tavern just off Broadway. The proprietor, a greasy man with one blind eye, had bitten the piece and examined it for teeth marks before agreeing to the deal. The knee buckles had gone to a King's Wharf chandler for a supply of biscuit and some musty flour.

On the fourth day, Phoebe, trailing three children, presents herself first thing in the morning at the Board of Refugees office taking her place in the queue that stretches out into the street. After two hours a spindly clerk with inky hands directs her to the nearby office of Colonel Roger Morris, Inspector of Refugee Claims.

Morris, a sour expression on his face, looks up from his papers and eyes Phoebe and her brood suspiciously. "Yes Madame, what can I do for you?"

"I pray sir, I am in the city, alone with five children, without any resources. We are hungry and need shelter."

"Indeed, in that predicament you are not alone. In any case who are you Madame, or should I say, who is your husband? Is he anyone I might know? I'm guessing he's with one of those wretched provincial corps, Johnson's or Jessup's. Am I right?"

"My husband is Robert Land, an express for Colonel Robinson and Sir Henry. Perhaps you've heard of them?"

The effect on Morris is immediate. The pinched face creases into a fawning smile and he lifts his arms as if in surrender. When he speaks the sneering edge in his voice is gone "Why didn't you say so, Madame? One of Colonel Robinson's Guides and Pioneers. An express for Sir Henry, oh yes, we certainly must take care of his family."

Grabbing quill in front of him he scribbles across a piece of parchment, signs his name and then, as if remembering something, excuses himself and leaves the room, paper in hand.

Five minutes later he returns with an even more cringing grin and hands Phoebe an order authorizing provisions and firewood, endorsed by Clinton's aide-de-camp.

"Major Andre apologizes that there's no decent accommodation available in the city," Morris says, "but he could arrange something temporary if Mrs. Land were willing to share with other unfortunate families…?"

On Water Street near the East River the two-storey house that had once been formidable was now simply forlorn. It had been occupied first by American soldiers and then, until quite recently by Hessian troops. The front door now marked with the King's cipher, GR, to indicate it was Rebel property seized by the crown. Woodwork and wainscoting have been stripped for fires, sconces torn from the walls, tiles from the roof. Many windows were broken and some of the downstairs rooms had been used to stable horses.

For all its sorry state however, there is no shortage of tenants. Every room is occupied and Phoebe is sincerely grateful when the red-eyed, Connecticut widow with two small babies agrees to share her pair of cramped rooms.

Phoebe walks into the back garden where weeds now grew among the clutter of roof tiles, fragments of wicker baskets, cracked chamber pots and the bones of a large animal, blinks back the tears she feels welling up and takes stock: She is alone with her children in a strange, dangerous city without resources, dependent on the charity of an indifferent military. Her husband is either in gaol or gone to Fort Niagara. Her oldest son is in gaol. Her home on the Delaware no longer exists. In fact her old life no longer exists but somehow she will carry on. Abel, she knows will soon return to the city. Maybe Robert will come to get them. And if the British discover some resolve and win this war they might even return to the Delaware.

As spring rolls on into summer the Land family quickly works out a survival routine. To earn money, Phoebe does laundry and mending for soldiers. The washing must be lugged by hand around Beekman's Swamp to the Fresh Water Pond—a journey of about half a mile—and carried back heavily wet to be hung in the garden. Kate and her sister have cleared part of the back garden and planted vegetables.

Sarah Barnes, the Connecticut widow whose husband was killed on the Burgoyne expedition, proves a resourceful friend. After two years in the city she knows her way and directs Phoebe to merchants who are honest and sympathetic. She is also able to alert the newcomers to the dangers on the streets—robberies, assaults, drunken brawls and even murders are not uncommon.

Sarah knows shops on Dock Street and Wall Street where fishheads and stewing bones can oftentimes be had for a few coppers, where tired greens and wilted vegetables can be found, where stale bread sells for half price.

Such supplements are necessary, for the army provisions—salt pork, beef and flour—are often spoiled. Phoebe and children over six, draw half rations—half pound of flour, six ounces of salt pork, four ounces of peas and four ounces of brown rice once a week. Children under six draw quarter rations. The salt meat which comes in barrels from Ireland is often maggoty, the butter rancid, the peas mouldy, and the flour adulterated with meal and even floor sweepings.

But despite their obvious hardships, Phoebe knows thousands are worse off. Poor Loyalists, or their orphaned children, with no resources or influential protectors might, if they are fortunate, end up in the almshouse. Many simply live in streets taking shelter where they can find it and beg for their daily bread.

And yet, amidst this widespread poverty there is much evidence of private affluence most of it funded by war profiteering and widespread corruption. Theatres and amusements flourish, the better shops are full of fine goods and groceries including imported cheeses, dried fruits, nuts and extensive baked goods. The new rich sleep on feather beds, sip Madeira from Irish crystal, dine off damask linen and enjoy cricket, horseracing, fox hunting, cock-fighting, golf and even bull-baiting.

Abel, who lives in army barracks, is a regular visitor. He splits wood for his mother, brings meat he's been able to buy from the commissary and takes the younger children for walks around the city. He has stopped coming at night though for robbers, drunken louts and naval press gangs rove the streets. Despite the outraged protests of Loyalists the Royal Navy continues to snatch young men off the streets to fill crew complements.

Phoebe and Sarah, by pooling resources and ingenuity, have established a household of sorts in their Water Street rooms. The pot is nearly always full of hearty, if plain, fare. Phoebe and Kate attend a makeshift school twice a week and in turn are helping to instruct Robert and Ephraim. Both have cooked, darned for, and even nursed, the British and German troops billeted in the neighbourhood and in return are under their unofficial protection. A drunken grenadier who accosts Phoebe on the street is rudely handled and sent on his way by a section of Irish dragoons living nearby.

The soldiers, who miss their own families, will sometimes bring the children a small piece of unsweetened chocolate, which grated in hot milk with nutmeg and sugar, affords an especial treat. Or on the rare occasions when soda and raisins are found the girls bake hobnails and snickerdoodles in the hearth's tin oven.

Occasionally an old neighbour brings news from the Delaware but there is no word from Robert until the end of September. An army clerk, doling out rations, hands Phoebe a folded page, closed with a stiff wax seal.

Easton, Pennsylvania
My Dear Phoebe:

Please forgive my long silence as I have not been at liberty to write concerning my situation. It is sufficient to say the last six months have been a trial which I Heartily pray never to repeat. Thanks to some old friends I expect to be at large soon & will forward more details via the first safe hand. My greatest affection to the children, I remain

Your loving husband,
Robert

November, 1780

 C&

"A man was hanged this morning for piloting some people through the back woods."
—Thomas Hughes

Fall lurches towards winter—the leaves change their colours, the days become crisper, the nights longer. Heavy grey rainclouds stay for days. Ralph Morden, looking, watching through the tiny window in the courthouse gaol, finds himself increasingly in thoughts of spring.

In the two weeks since his sentence was confirmed, he's found himself drawn back to that May morning in Mount Bethel.

Captain Land and three others came by just before dawn, knocking softly on the cabin door. Morden shivered as he left Ann's warm closeness to pull on leather breeches and a coarse, cloth coat.

A quick look around the simple cabin to the sleeping children, he gathered haversack and bed roll, shouldered the heavy flour pack and stepped out into the gathering early light.

With silent nods to each other, they set off.

Walking through the rolling hills that reached to the mountain ridge he was struck how astonishingly green the countryside appeared. It was a mild, overcast day—heavy rain had fallen the night before—and the air had a rich, sweetness he couldn't seem to get his fill of.

Years before he'd tried to till the stony, thin plot but found he hadn't the patience. So he left the small vegetable plot for Ann to manage while he roamed the mountains and valleys of the Delaware and Susquehanna, often in the company of Indians.

Like most Quakers he tried to avoid taking sides in the war but blood and circumstance made that difficult. Three younger brothers had already joined Loyalist regiments—one died at Oriskany—and Morden, who was not born in the Society of Friends, felt the tug of loyalty, to England, the land of his birth.

Quakers, particularly in Penn's Colony, had to face the growing anger of Patriots who saw their lack of support for the revolution as treasonous. Refusing to bear arms, pay taxes to support the war or even to accept the currency of the fledgling republic, Quakers were imprisoned and had property seized.

Morden himself had to endure the abuse of neighbours who said Quakers were just using their religion as an excuse to avoid army service.

In truth Morden was offended to be called a coward and at times, hard pressed to honour the Quaker precept of turning the other cheek. In deference to his wife though, he bit his tongue. Her family had been Quakers for generations and by marrying him she had risked being cast out of the Society.

Morden eked a meagre living buying furs from Indians who knew him to be honest and fair in his dealings. On one such buying expedition on the Susquehanna a few years earlier he'd met a dark-eyed white man traveling in the company of two Mohawks.

An intense man who rarely smiled, he had questioned Morden—asked where he lived, asked about any brothers. It not being in Morden's nature or religion to be devious, he answered with full candour.

The stranger had listened carefully and then asked if he ever worked as a guide.

Morden said he had, though not for gain, as it was his obligation to help where there was need. After sharing some bannock over a small fire they parted and Morden hadn't seen him again until he turned up in Mount Bethel that May.

He introduced himself as Captain Land, said he had a party heading for Fort Niagara. Would Morden help them across Kittatinny Ridge and perhaps accompany them?

"You might get to see your brothers," Land had said, "find something you thought you lost."

The idea was attractive to Morden. He'd been to the mouth of the Niagara once, seen the mighty cataract. An old trader told him that beyond the river, between the stone ridge and the lake, lay mile after mile of fertile land.

Maybe, thought Morden, if the Rebels continue to persecute the Quakers, his family might find a better home at Niagara.

And so he agreed, and on that fragrant spring morning found himself leading Land and his party north from Mount Bethel towards a cleft in the Blue Mountains known as Tott's Gap.

The land rose gradually for several miles through graceful valleys and perfectly rounded hills dotted with rude farms and tired-looking horses before rising sharply at the base of the range.

From his hard bench in Easton gaol Morden could see it all and he missed it like he'd never missed anything in his life. He could see the yellow feet and beaks on the ducks, the soft, long eyelashes of the old mare, the tiny white strawberry blossoms and smell the pollen-rich air.

Captain Land had three younger men with him—two Pennsylvanians— Oziah McCarty and James Griffin and a British solider, Elisha Barton. From what he could gather, all intended to join the Indian Department at Fort Niagara.

Each carried a musket, Griffin and Barton, standard army issue Brown Bess, McCarty and Land, short-barreled Indian trade guns.

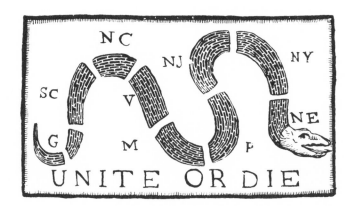

Everyone carried a 30-pound backpack of flour, one man's ration for the four-week journey.

Ascending into the mountains they passed easily through hardwood forests of oak and hickory, many of the trees thickly wrapped with wild vines. The grey, lichen-covered rocks clinked musically underfoot, the men waved their hats to whisk away the early black flies. A brilliant Tanager tracked their progress, flitting curiously from tree to tree.

Late in the afternoon they reached the gap and rested, smoking pipes and listening to the wind sough through the pines. Ahead of them lay the bush path white traders had been using for 50 years and Indians for centuries before that.

It was a warm evening, the path was open and clear, Land had chosen Tott's Gap through the mountains to avoid Rebel patrols guarding the more northerly Delaware Water Gap. By swinging south of Fort Penn, Morden said, they should be clear by the next day.

The small party moved easily, confident no militia would be out late in the day, particularly during spring planting.

They were crossing a rocky slope with the sun slanting low on the horizon when Morden heard something from the high ground just behind him—a soft, muffled click followed by a quick shuffle of feet.

He was turning to look when a voice called out: "Make ready!" and he heard a dozen musket hammers click into firing position.

"Throw down your firelocks," came the call, "and we'll spare your miserable lives."

"In a pig's ear," Land hollered back as he and McCarty threw themselves to the ground.

"Give fire!" came the command.

Land and McCarty who had been lower on the slope were just unslinging their muskets as flints crashed into steel frissons and the ragged Rebel volley thundered overhead and echoed through the mountains.

Dense white smoke covered the area, so thick that Morden could taste the sulphur. Barton, taking cover behind a rock returned fire while the militia struggled in the failing light to ram paper cartridges and lead balls.

Another volley cracked and splattered into the grey rocks, it's echo rolling off over the hills. In the silence Land counted the interval between volleys and waited. On command they fired again and Land sprang up and turned to run.

The last gun in the Rebel line had not fired. It's owner cursed, recocked and squeezed the trigger. A tiny spark hit the priming charge and the steel gun bucked and thumped into his shoulder.

Land hurtled forward and down. No time to get his hands down for protection his head crashed into the grey rocks, one arm folded under him.

"Captain Land!" McCarty screamed.

Shaking his head Land managed to rise to one knee as McCarty cut away his pack, wrapped an arm around his back and dragged him off into the gathering darkness.

Quickly the patrol scrambled down the incline.

Morden, who hadn't moved since the action began, was roughly pushed into a sitting position beside Barton.

"Where's Land?" the officer called, as his men spread out over the rocks.

"If he be not dead, he's dying for certain," said the man whose shot felled him. Indeed, Morden could not see how it could be otherwise for

even in the gloom, the rocks where Land had fallen and his discarded knapsack were stained dark and glistening with blood. One of the militia picked up Land's tricorn, thumbed the thick beaver felt and put it on.

The officer had then called Morden a damned Tory and demanded to know where the party was going.

Morden, with no guile, told the truth. Fort Niagara. Said he was a Quaker rendering these men aid, no more than he'd done for many Patriots.

As far as the British pass found in his haversack, he had it in case he was separated from the party.

"You're a fool Morden," the officer said, "but you're a lucky fool. If we'd taken that villain Land alive he'd hang for sure. You, you're just going to gaol."

But it hadn't worked out that way.

In Easton, where the local magistrate was still furious that Land had jumped bail after two prominent citizens posted a bond, Morden was charged with treason. A British spy inciting the Indians. Fed up with Quakers in general they resolved to make Morden an example. Three judges heard the case, one of them had no use for Friends whatsoever. And the prosecutor—a relative of Benedict Arnold's wife—was determined to show what he thought of British spies. The case of the treasonous Quaker caused much excitement in Easton. Each day, curious onlookers filled the courthouse.

Morden, who began the trial thinking the charges against him could not be proved, soon discovered the court chose to disbelieve nearly everything he said. His defence of being a Quaker and offering help where needed, was, according to the court, no defence at all.

The jury, nearly all of whom were known to Morden, found him guilty. The chief justice, a cold, haughty man, pronounced the sentence "that he be hanged by the neck till he be dead."

Elisha Barton, the escaped British prisoner taken with him, upon payment of a good behaviour bond, was set free.

Ann comes to see him after the trial. She nearly weeps to see how old and haggard he looks. Morden sits and holds her hand and they pray together. They talk about each of their eight children.

"Is there no hope?" she asks, watching him with red-rimmed eyes. Morden, locking his eyes on hers, slowly shakes his head.

Ann shifts her gaze away from his, biting her lower lip until she can taste blood. "My heart is so full I fear it bursts! God keep you Ralph Morden and protect us from ruin. I am forever undone."

All this Morden reflects on as late fall darkens his tiny cell.

They come for him in the cold, pre-dawn dark of a late November morning. His hands bound, he is taken by ox-cart up the steep path to Gallows Hill. A small guard of troops watches while a hemp noose is snugged up under his chin. An ostler whips the ox, the cart creaks forward and Ralph Morden, thinking of spring on a cold November morn, is hanged.

May, 1780

‹β

"After many fatigues and hardships…"
—Robert Land petition

Land can hear voices. Low and muffled like they're coming through a stack of wet blankets. They fade and then return, slowly building strength. There's a crushing pain behind his eyes and a strange floating sensation. He strains to open his eyes. The voices belong to McCarty and someone else. They are standing in front of the hearth in a small cabin. Land realizes he's lying on a pallet. His vision partially obscured by the bottom part of a bandage wrapped around his head.

"Oziah" he whispers, "where are we?"

"In the hills near Goshen?"

"Rebels caught us in an ambuscade. You took a ball in the back—it never got through your knapsack but you smacked your head on rock and bled some. We crawled off in the dark. They got the Quaker and Barton though, I expect."

Land struggles to remember but all he can find is a jumble of shots and shouts that ended with a heavy, black weight pushing him down, crushing him.

They are a week in the cabin before Land is steady enough to travel. McCarty wants to continue to Niagara but Land is set on New York.

"You do as you please," he tells the younger man, "I've got to see my family. Rebels are bound to hang or shoot me. Maybe it's time the Indian Department gave them someone else to aim at."

And so the pair slowly and painfully—for Land is still wracked with fever—shamble across New York and New Jersey. They travel only a few hours each night until at last they reach British lines on Staten Island. An army supply boat takes them to New York and a 20-minute walk gets them crosstown.

Phoebe, who is just leaving the house with William, sees them in the distance coming up Water Street and wonders idly about such ragged men.

Something about the way the older one carries himself is familiar, the thrust and purpose of his walk. A cry catches in her throat. She steps to the street and just stares, her heart and eyes filling with a mixture of joy and anguish. Joy for the first sight of her man in more than three years, anguish for the wear that war and captivity have laid on him.

He walks trying to ignore the tears that blur his vision as his children flank out on either side of his wife. William the youngest still clutching his mother's petticoat, Kate already a young woman and Phoebe not far behind. Robert and Ephraim gape with open mouths for, in truth, they can hardly remember what their father looks like.

In a crush that blocks the walkway they come together in a silent embrace that Land wishes will never end. Kneeling down in front of the children, he takes from his haversack the tiny wooden figures carved at Minisink. A bear for Will, a horse for Robert, a wolf for Ephraim, an eagle for Kate and a turtle for Phoebe.

That night, long after the children have gone to bed, Robert and Phoebe sit together like the lovers they were a quarter of century before in New York. By the light of a single candle they face across a small table, her hands exploring every crease and scar on his face until he reaches up and gently places both of them between his own hard hands and watches the tenderness in her eyes as it washes across her face.

He wants to speak but the words won't form. He wants to apologize for the pain and hardship he has brought on his family, the sorrow his pride has wrought, the grief this God-damned war had caused. But all he can do is probe Phoebe's soft brown eyes and caress her hands. Safe in the proof of his loving family.

In the morning, Phoebe insists Land see the army surgeon. He is fat, with pudgy hands and is constantly mopping rheumy eyes with a handkerchief. He lifts the muslin rag covering the still-raw scalp wound, sniffs it and tells Land "I've seen men die of less and recover from worse; you'll likely be fine in another month or so. I expect you're febrile so take one of these every day."

Land suspiciously examines the small tin box of pills.

"I reckon a dose of boiled fox lung is superior physic," the surgeon adds, "but there aren't many left in New York, the hounds have run them all down."

Over the weeks under Phoebe's care, he slowly mends bolstered by the extra rations a petition to Clinton has secured.

In August a brig carrying refugees from Georgia docks and is found to be carrying a putrid fever. The discovery, however, comes after most of the crew has already gone ashore. Within three days a fever epidemic has broken out in the city and both young Phoebe and William are afflicted. The surgeon prescribes tincture of bark and balsam. The girl's temperature breaks but William develops a dry cough. The surgeon bleeds the lad and tells Phoebe to burn sulphur to clear the air.

In September when the heat begins to drain from the summer he appears to rally but the fever returns and his little frame is wracked with coughing. All through it he clutches the tiny basswood bear.

When he dies, a small wasted figure on a straw mattress, Phoebe summons all her strength to provide calm and comfort for the rest of the family. Kate leads the children in prayer.

After the initial shock and sorrow, Land becomes furious. The night after they bury the boy in the Trinity Church graveyard—attended by a disinterested clerk—he fuels his rage with black rum, ranting about sow gelding surgeons and Rebel poltroons who have driven his family to live like dogs in this cursed city.

Outside, on the streets, the "cursed city" buzzes over the defection of Benedict Arnold, one of Washington's best generals. The initial optimism that the tide of war might turn, quickly fades however. Arnold has not been able to deliver the key Hudson River stronghold at West Point. And, his defection has cost Clinton's aide-de-camp, John Andre, his life. The city is rife with rumours of a French invasion. And from North Carolina comes word of a stunning rebel victory at a place called King's Mountain.

CB

"If you should ever have occasion to send an express to these parts,
I can recommend him as very proper to be entrusted with it."
—Brigadier-General Watson Powell

Two months later Land is still quietly seething with anger and grief when a messenger arrives. He is summoned to a brick mansion near the French Church, the home of Colonel Beverley Robinson, head of the army's Guides and Pioneers.

Instructed to wait in the foyer by a liveried servant, Land can not help noticing Robinson denies himself few comforts. In the grate a cheery fire pumps heat into the high-ceilinged room, the floors are covered with soft woollen carpets, the walls with paintings and ornately framed mirrors. In this one room alone are more candles than his family burns in an entire month.

Presently he is ushered into a salon, where Robinson, a tall, imposing man in maroon waistcoat and fine moleskin breeches, is sitting behind a delicate Chippendale table. Beside him, a plate of tiny Chinese oranges.

"Ah Land," he says in a voice still inflected with the accents of his native Virginia, "please sit. I trust you are recovered from your wounds?"

Land, bowing his chin to his chest, sits down. "Thank you sir, I am."

"Good, then I have some important work for you. How soon can you leave?"

"Begging your pardon but I am not at liberty to leave New York at this time."

"Really sir? And may I ask why not?"

"We have just buried my youngest, Colonel Robinson, he was three,

my wife and I are sore distressed. I have spent nearly four years on service. I can't leave them right now."

"Hmmm, well, I am much aggrieved to hear that sir," says Robinson his voice softening. "I know family is the source of a man's true strength and no wound cuts deeper or closer to the heart than one that hurts his family but all the same Land there's a war going on and duty is the highest calling. I too have just suffered a deep, personal loss, my dear friend, the estimable Major Andre, he was like a nephew to me—but I'm still required to serve my monarch."

"With all respect colonel, I've never shrunk from my duty. Never asked for favour but my familys lives in an icehouse on the East River, we haven't enough fuel for cooking let alone heat. This morning the mingoes and inkwells were frozen solid. We live on wormy hardtack and pork that's not fit for a cur. The place is rife with vermin and contagion. We're cold and hungry and one of us is dead. I can't ask my wife to countenance any more travails. I won't be making this trip."

A look, half amazement and half irritation, passes over Robinson's face. "Good Heavens man, I'd no idea you were short of fuel. I'll have some cord wood brought around first thing in the morning and I'll speak to commissary about the victuals. You're absolutely right, you can't leave your family in want, but at the same time sir you must understand the Crown has urgent need of your talents. There are expresses that must reach Fort Niagara before full winter and you're the only guide I've got who can make that trip. I give you my word as a gentleman, I'll personally see to your family's welfare if you'll go to Fort Niagara for me.

Will you do this for me Robert Land?"

Land, who has been sitting and staring into the grate fire, stands and turns to look at Robinson, a look of weary resignation on his face.

"How soon am I to leave?"

When he gets back to the family's rooms later that night, Phoebe is sitting at the table, a single candle burning in front of her. Without a word she passes her husband a folded letter.

He reads slowly, his lips soundlessly forming the words, then he stops, his eyes widen: "They hanged

Morden? They hanged a Quaker? What kind of men are these? He never bore arms, never caused violence to anyone. He lived by the laws of God. He was simply our guide. It's me they really wanted to hang but they've took Morden in my stead."

"Did he have family," Phoebe asks.

"Yes, a wife and eight children. They took Morden's life instead of mine."

The next day Land is gone, heading west to Niagara. Just before he leaves, a carter escorted by two soldiers, delivers a load of firewood, two barrels of salt pork, a sack of potatoes, a wheel of cheese and a packet of green tea. "From the colonel's private reserve," he smiles tipping his hat to Phoebe.

1781

ℭℬ

"You cannot conceive, nor can any language describe, the distress that all ranks of people here have been thrown into…universal despair and phrenzy prevails…"
—Benjamin Thompson

"The open enemies of Great Britain have gained their point…this 'peace' brings none to my heart…"
—Edward Winslow

Early in the new year Ephraim is briefly sick and Phoebe, alarmed at the possibility of losing another child, insists he be baptized immediately, the brief ceremony conducted in the temporary quarters of Trinity Church off Broadway.

To Phoebe's amazement, Land arrives just before the Christening looking thin and haggard. He's travelled from Niagara to Montreal in two weeks, then down the Lake Champlain/Hudson River corridor by sleigh in only 10 days.

In February Abel and Oziah McCarty, who have been with the renegade general Benedict Arnold and Colonel John Graves Simcoe on raids into Virginia, return to New York. They tell tales of fiery depredations up and down the James River and routing the Rebel's Prussian drillmaster, Von Steuben.

As summer approaches though, prospects of British victory diminish. Washington himself boldly inspects British defensive works from the other side of the Hudson. In New Jersey a great Rebel army is gathering; it's said they'll invade New York as soon as the French fleet arrives. A huge encampment has been marked out on the Jersey shore. They've even built bake-ovens to provide troops with bread. Clinton, for one, is certain

a siege is imminent and will not venture out to meet the Americans.

But then in August the Rebel army abruptly leaves, marching south to rendezvous with the French fleet and set a trap for the British army in Virginia. In New York, Clinton dithers. Only after word arrives that Cornwallis is under siege by a larger French and American force does he act.

A relief force, including Abel Land, finally sails from New York on October 19.

Four days later New Yorkers are startled to hear gunfire from the New Jersey side of the Hudson. It sounds, some say, like the celebration of a great victory. The following day, a Rebel delegation, crossing under a flag of truce to conduct a prisoner exchange, confirms the city's worst fear. Lord Cornwallis, outnumbered two-to-one and unable to retreat, has surrendered an army of 8,000 to a combined Franco-American force.

Except for the shouting, and a few more minor skirmishes, the war is effectively over. For the Crown's loyal American allies the unthinkable has happened. The nightmare that haunted their lives for seven years has come true.

The effect on tens of thousands of Loyalists in New York is catastrophic. They are now pariahs and exiles in their homeland for British power is no more in the colonies. Those who stood with the Crown now realize the day of reckoning is at hand and they stand to forfeit not only property and freedom, but quite possibly their lives. Washington refuses to consider American-born Loyalists serving with the British army as prisoners of war. This distinction makes them traitors and candidates for the gallows.

Betrayal is the word on every lip. Britain, whose commitment to the war was ever suspect, has caved in and only innocent optimists and fools still talk of the might and honour of British arms.

BE IT REMEMBERED!

THAT on the 17th of October, 1781, Lieutenant-General Earl CORNWALLIS, with above Five thousand British Troops, surrendered themselves Prisoners of War to his Excellency Gen. GEORGE WASHINGTON, Commander in Chief of the allied Forces of France and America.

LAUS DEO!

As the war winds down, the flood of Loyalist refugees, soldiers and prisoners pouring into New York further stretches the resources of an already dangerously overcrowded city. Many families, without the means to buy food and fuel at black market prices, lead desperately wretched lives. There is much madness and some, unable to face the material loss of their fall from grace, take refuge in suicide.

The speculation is that the Crown will re-settle refugees in Canada, probably in the maritime colony of Nova Scotia. Everyone knows they can't stay in the United States.

Early in the new year of 1782, Land is summoned once again to the Robinson's mansion and returns to tell Phoebe he is returning to the frontiers as a courier between Fort Niagara and Quebec.

"Why?" Phoebe asks. "This war's lost and you've been marked. The Rebels tried to kill you twice. The next time will be your last and we'll be no better off than Ralph Morden's family."

"Phoebe we can never live among these people again. You know that. Too much blood has been shed, too many lives lost. The hate is too strong. We'll never go back to the Delaware. They say we may all end up in Canada. If God wills it and the Crown grants land, I want to be sure there's no question the Land family has a sound claim and entitlement. Besides you can draw my wage here and you'll have one less mouth to feed."

April, 1783
❧

"We have very fair accommodation in the cabin although it contains six families beside our own…"
—Sarah Frost

For ten days the fleet has been gathering at anchor off Sandy Hook about 12 miles south of the city in New York's Lower Bay. More than 50 sail are being assembled to evacuate the first wave of refugees from the last British stronghold in the American colonies.

The spring nights are raw with cold Atlantic fogs rolling through the aging transports. Phoebe's extended family of sons, daughters and in-laws together with two other families are sharing one cabin. At night the combination of crowded bodies, poor ventilation, crying babies and the constant creaking and rocking at anchor, makes sleep almost impossible. The days are filled with endless teas, cribbage parties and the occasional trip ashore to wander the lonely, rolling dunes.

For the Loyalists packed aboard the transports, the last 10 months have seen the realization of their deepest, innermost fears. Not even the most skeptical of Crown supporters could have foreseen the complete collapse of British resolve. Having lost the war, cynics say, the Crown has now contrived to lose the peace as well.

Late last summer when news arrived the British government had conceded unconditional independence for all thirteen colonies, the Loyalist population of 33,000 was struck dumb, the phrase "we are ruined" was on every lip.

As implications of the total British capitulation began to sink in, a mood of intense bitterness and sense of betrayal grew among the Loyalists. Indeed, so profound was the anger among local militia

units that for several weeks authorities feared an open revolt. For many the hurt inflicted by their fellow-Americans in war paled beside the treachery of their allies, the British government.

Some families have tried to reclaim pre-war property but such is the hostility and violence of their reception that any thoughts of going home are quickly abandoned.

Throughout the fall as refugees from the abandoned outposts of Savannah and Charleston flowed into the overstuffed city, newspapers, like James Rivington's *New York Gazetteer*, were full of favourable descriptions of Nova Scotia. They described the rich soil, the abundant forests—and truly, for the majority of refugees, the Crown's offer of 200 acres and two years' provisions in the northern colony is their

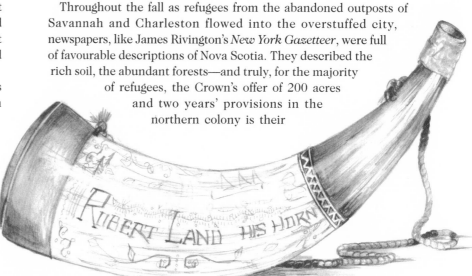

only recourse. Few Loyalists are rich enough to go to England or the West Indies.

By the spring of 1783, New York was a heaving, mess of humanity. The streets were full of troops, British and German regulars—many of them newly released prisoners of war—and thousands of green-coated provincials. The former there in hope of going home, the latter in fear of Patriot ropes. At public meetings in March, where the preliminary articles of peace were read, naught but groans and hisses are heard attended by curses on the name of the King and his ministers.

Already some of the bolder Rebels have dared venture into New York to lay early claim to property abandoned after the British invasion. Every day there are auctions as departing Loyalists sell off their belongings. On occasions where Rebel and Loyalist might meet in the street, only the presence of British soldiers prevents violence.

Phoebe and her family come on board the transport with what they can carry—blankets, a few tools, clothing and some food—pickles, potatoes and cheese—to supplement the ship's ration.

A spring dawn and northwest winds finally push the great fleet out to sea. In an afternoon calm Abel and Oziah fish mackerel over the side. Two windless days out the flotilla disappears in a fog. The only contacts are the ships' bells and the hourly gun from the commodore's vessel.

Before noon on the 12th day the ships clear Cape Sable and land is sighted. Early the following morning Phoebe awakes to the rumble and scrape of anchor chains. Drawing a cloak over her shoulders she goes on deck and by the grey dawn light catches the first glimpse of her new home.

Certainly it is a fine harbour but the surrounding land is precipitous, barren rock broken only by occasional stands of brush and scrub pine. The only signs of settlement are a pair of mismatched blockhouses surrounded by a small cluster of buildings on a limestone cliff overlooking the harbour. It is, a fellow refugee remarks, "the roughest land I ever saw."

A damp breeze ripples across the harbour, Phoebe snugs her cloak, stares to the rocky shore and mouths a silent prayer for strength and forbearance.

A few hours later, the Land clan lingers in the shadow of Fort Howe while Abel and McCarty gather up three grey canvas tents, a stack of blankets, axes, cast-iron pots and a promise of building material, seeds and fertile land farther up the Saint John River.

Within six months this backwater settlement, where Mi'kmaq and Maliseet still outnumber whites, will become home to 14,000 refugees and boast well over 1,000 houses. Within a year it will be a separate colony. But for many of these Loyalists it will never be home.

February, 1788

"The lands as we came along seemed extremely good, heavy timbered...all lofty of their kind."
—Patrick Campbell

Land's snowshoes scratch a slow rhythm over the snow crust covering the bay. It's high winter and a grey squall lingering over the open water of the lake sends an occasional flurry of snow whirling across the ice. A large black dog lopes behind him stepping carefully into the compressed snow. Directly ahead two Mississauga Indians are on their knees in a section where they have burrowed through the grainy snow to the ice.

"Aaniin" says Land in greeting. *"Aaniin, waabshkiiyed"* comes the response from the older of the two. Around them lie the stiff, frozen carcasses of pickerel and bass.

They have used a broadhead axe to chop through the ice and make a hole as broad as a man's shoulders. One takes a small carved fish and presses a piece of lead shot into its wooden body. Secured on a length of sinew it is lowered into the water. In the man's right hand he holds a light, double-pronged spear or *nit* about 10 feet long. While he lies at the edge of the hole, the other brave covers him and the hole with a blanket. For a few minutes he remains poised as if frozen, then in a flash the spear is thrust down, the blanket is torn away and— expertly impaled through the head just behind the eyes—a great pike, as tall as a man, emerges snapping and writhing from the hole. A blow of the axe stills the jaws and the older of the two smiles and hands Land the spear and the wooden lure. Dropping to his belly, Land positions himself over the bottle-green water, cocks his spear arm with spear and sinks the lure.

As the blanket descends the dark waters are immediately illuminated, as if lighted from below. Twenty feet down Land can see pebbles and weeds gently waving. Jerking his hand the lure moves and soon there are three dark shapes moving menacingly around it. While one makes a lunge at the lure, Land draws a bead on one of the onlookers and thrusts the spear down, hard and fast.

With a shout the blanket is torn away and the *nit* recovered, one of the prongs driven through the rear of a small pickerel, just ahead of the tail.

Jokes are made about the paleface's poor aim. Land produces a round loaf of bread from his pack that is cut and eaten. Two of the largest fish, frozen solid, and bound together with a length of sinew are given the white man as he leaves. *Baa maa pii miinwaa ka waabmin* see you later *Miigwech mee-wetch* thank you.

Fish are a large part of his diet—pickerel, trout, black bass, white fish and salmon abound in the bay. On a summer's night two men in a canoe with a pitch pine torch, can easily harvest hundreds of fish using the *nit*. In the fall the mouths of streams emptying into the lake teem with log-sized salmon that can be taken by net or spear.

There is wildfowl in profusion, plenty of venison and a variety of small game including rabbit, squirrel, muskrat, turkey, woodcock and pheasant. Indeed, food is not a problem on this bay of plenty where he has prospered in a few short years.

In the first year he built a rough bark hut, cleared three acres and planted his first crop—potatoes and turnips—between the stumps, followed by winter wheat in the fall. Seeds and tools were part of the supplies provided refugees by the Crown.

The following spring Land built a cabin of squared white pine, harvesting the enormous timber that grew nearly as tall as the stone ridge itself. One tree was sufficient for eight or ten logs. With a froe and maul he split cedar shingles for the roof and used inlet clay to finish the chimney and caulk the walls. The door hung on wooden hinges and a single window admits light through heavy, oiled paper.

Land is no longer alone at the head of the lake. Fellow war refugees, some from the Delaware and the Susquehanna valleys, have settled nearby. Joseph Brant and 1,800 New York Iroquois live within a two days' journey on the Grand River. An itinerant fur trader, Richard Beasley conducts business on the heights overlooking the bay exchanging supplies and trade goods for beaver, fox, deer, bear and martin pelts. From Beasley, Land hears that Ann Morden, widow of Ralph Morden, along with three sons, three daughters and three grandchildren, has settled on the Niagara River at Queenston.

Land no longer relies on victuals from Fort Niagara. He is becoming self-sufficient as the rich lands fronting the bay yield an abundance of crops including wheat, beans, flax and pumpkins.

It is, as Land and many of the refugees have discovered, better than the holdings they lost in the American colonies. Yet for all his prospects the wounds of war still ache.

Uncertainty and fear are constant companions. The treason of former friends, the treachery of allies has left Loyalists uncertain of the very ground under them. Who can be trusted? The Crown that sold out the Loyalists with a half-hearted war effort and then rolled over in the peace negotiations?

The nonsense rhyme of a popular tavern ditty has more reason:

> *If buttercups buzzed after the bee*
> *If boats were on land, churches on sea*
> *If ponies rode men and grass ate the cows*

If summer were spring and the other way 'round
Then all of the world would be upside down

Land has passed many a night in torment, wracked by guilt that he has failed his family, terrified the damage may be permanent.

Lost in thought and the rhythmn of his snowshoes, Land is mildly surprised how quickly he and the dog have reached the homestead. On the ridge a pale winter sun is disappearing as he enters the cabin. Crossing to the hearth he coaxes some embers to life, ignites a wood shaving and lights the scrap of linen in a shallow metal dish, half-full of raccoon tallow. The flame on the betty lamp splutters and flickers and a pool of dim yellow light spreads across the hearth.

A pot is swung over the remains of the fire, Land pours some dark rum into a tin mug and settles into a crude, flat-seated chair facing the hearth.

From the inside of his beaver hat he takes a creased and folded piece of paper, opens and reads:

Saint John, New Brunswick
My Dearest Robert:

One of the naval officers is to travel to the Upper Lakes & I have asked him to carry this as far as Fort Niagara. I trust this letter finds you well. We are facing another winter in this place. I am not at all certain we can endure. The fogs are endless, snow falls but never enough to insulate our shelters from the wind. Firewood is scarce. It rains constantly from May to mid-July the mosquitoes are a constant curse. The soil is exceedingly poor and forbidding. Despite considerable labour by Abel, Oziah and Robert our six acres yielded but nine bushels of wheat this year. We live on Irish salt pork, cod and oats. Ephraim had red measles in the fall. I do not believe we can ever prosper in this land. I have word from former Delaware neighbours that John is returned to Cushetunk and married there. Dare I hope there is a chance we might all return? I long to see this family restored. We have not lived together for 13 years now, you have grandchildren that have never seen you. May providence deliver us. I remain your obedient wife.

Phoebe

℃ℬ

*"Captain Brant who is well acquainted with European manners,
received us with much politeness and hospitality."*
—Patrick Campbell

In the morning after a restive night when fitful wind sent puffs of smoke and ash back into the cabin, Land is up before dawn. He blows enough life into the fire to heat some beechnut coffee, tucks a slab of cornbread into his haversack and leaves the cabin. Near the edge of his clearing he picks up the Indian path that snakes up to the top of the stony ridge and then leads south to the Grand River.

Trudging up the winding trail, he turns to watch a pale smudge of winter sun rise from the lake while whirlwinds of snow dance across the bay. It is cold but snugged inside a wool *capote,* his fur mittens and moccasins stuffed with cattail down, Land is warm and dry.

At the edge of the ridge the woods are lofty and thick but thin quickly as he tramps off swinging easily from foot to foot on the snowshoes. Occasionally a rabbit will break at his approach with the black dog, his breath smoking in the winter air, giving pursuit.

At noon he eats the cornbread, at dusk he stops at a trapper's cabin, the walls and ceiling hung with stretched and drying pelts. Most are common red fox but there are two sleek and lustrous black fox pelts the trapper claims will fetch enough to keep him in rum and hoe cake at least for six months.

Warmed at the fire and restored by a piece of cold venison, Land sleeps soundly to rise at dawn and resume his journey. By late afternoon he can see the chimney smoke of Brant's Town overlooking the frozen, meandering Grand.

In the years since the Six Nations left their ancestral lands in New York at the end of the war, a community has grown up here with a church, school and blacksmith. Most of the dwellings are simple cabins save one imposing two-storey structure extended to include a wing and a porch with the whole neatly fenced and topped with a staff flying the Kings colours.

To this house Land makes his way, fixing on the soft yellow light glowing from the ground floor windows.

Shedding snowshoes and climbing to the porch he is met at the door by a black servant dressed in ruffled shirt, coat and buckled shoes. The anteroom opens into the middle of the house where the hearth blazes with logs as big around as a man's thigh. Standing next to the fireplace is a man Land has not seen for nearly six years.

The face is fuller, the jowls heavier, the hair on the scalp lock not quite as lustrous but the skin is smooth and the eyes exactly as Land remembered. Dark, and wary. As usual he is dressed with care and style in a fine, apple-green coat with brass buttons, a black, silk scarf and buff, kerseymere breeches with silver knee buckles.

"Captain Brant," he calls, "*sago. Skanago?*"

"*Sago,*" Brant answers. "How are you Robert Land? I heard you were living at the head of the lake. The mosquitoes and the rattlesnakes in that slash haven't carried you off yet?"

"One of the blessings of winter Captain," Land replies with laugh, "it keeps them both in check."

"I expect from the look of you that you're living rough down there, like you're still on campaign. Where's your family?"

"They're still out in New Brunswick Captain, that's what I wished to speak with you about."

"Well certainly," Brant replies with an expansive smile, "but first we eat. My cook's spitted a joint of pork, I've dark rum and passable Madeira. My man will show you to your chambers, as soon as you're cleaned up, we'll dine."

Over a meal the likes of which Land has not seen since before the war— served on fine china, silver plate and thick damask—the two Indian Department veterans, toast the King and Queen, talk of old times and trade news of friends and enemies.

Finally, full of roast pork and sweet potato and fronting a crystal glass of port, Land gets down to the reason he's come.

"Captain Brant, the land I'm sitting on at the head of the lake is rich, the climate is mild and crops flourish. In truth it could be the best I've ever seen but therein lies my problem."

Brant, drops his glass to the table and cradling chin under his hand, says, "Indeed, do tell."

Clearing a space in front of him on the tablecloth, Land continues, "my wife Phoebe, and the rest of my family are in New Brunswick, struggling to scratch a living. The soil is mean, the climate harsh. Most certainly they

would be better off here but I fear to send for them as I have no title to my holdings at the head of the lake.

The land in New Brunswick," he says pointing to a spot on his right, "while poor, they own, free and clear. The land I occupy here," pointing directly in front of him, "is held strictly at the pleasure of the Crown. I live in fear of waking one morning to find some reduced

Provincial officer with the right sort of friends taking measure of my plot, and not being able to do anything about it. There is an unseemly scramble for property these days and considerable evidence of shady dealings in how it's being distributed."

Brant takes a long draught of his port and wipes his mouth with a folded napkin. "You are wise to be cautious Robert," he says. "If we've learned anything since the end of the war, it's that the Crown rarely has our interest at heart. Two years ago I journeyed to London and got naught but mealy words and treachery from those who have the ear of the King. I am fearful from experience.

Haldimand promised this land along the Grand was ours. North and south, from source to mouth, 'to enjoy for ever' he said. But when I try to sell a piece or give a present, the Crown says we have no title. I say, they have no honour. How can we be a free people if we have no control over our land?"

With that Brant stops and stares at the molten puddle of tallow that gathers on the candlestick base. The fire, in decline, puffs meekly, a wind off the river rattles the frosted windows, the tall clock in the corner ticks woodenly and somewhere a dog barks.

"If I were in your position Robert, I would stand fast. Stay where you are, and keep your family in New Brunswick until the head of the lake is surveyed. I've heard two years, maybe three, before that happens. Once your name's on the survey you can get a location ticket, and that's as good as a deed."

"That may well be," Land says, "but as part of Quebec we're still under French law in the upper country, Captain. Their concept of land tenure makes me very apprehensive. I want freehold. I want a deed. I lost 700 acres of the best land in Pennsylvania because Rebels—by the stroke of their legislative pen, declared I had no legal title. I swear that won't happen again."

Taking the decanter, Brant fills both their glasses. "That's true but many Loyalists are petitioning for a separate colony under British law that would guarantee property rights. I believe this will happen—not because it's fair but because it's in his Britannic majesty's best interest to encourage settlement here before the Yankees swallow the rest of his colonies. Settlers like you will be allowed to take root and grow because the British know that without such an anchor a Yankee flood could carry everything away.

Guy Carleton, who is now a Lord I'm told, is sympathetic to calls for English tenure and I believe it will come to be."

July, 1791

ℭß

"Stigmatized until the day of his death…"
—James Quinlan

Joseph Ross stands staring at the greying woman walking along the riverbank between two young men. There is something very familiar about her yet he can't quite place her.

He's seen dozens of families he knew before the war come scraggling back to the Upper Delaware with this wary, cautious look in their eyes. Initially they'd been driven off like dogs often accompanied by beatings and death threats. Only the high regard Ross had enjoyed before the war and his absolute refusal to leave saved him from a similar fate. Neighbours spit when he passed by and glared hostility but none had the nerve to run him off.

Gradually the rage cooled, although even now, nearly eight years after the last British soldier left New York, the term Tory is still the worst slur that could be cast on a family's character.

"Madame," he calls out, "may I be of assistance?"

Turning slowly, Phoebe takes a measure of the man addressing her.

"Indeed kind sir," she answers, "we seek to cross the river."

Hearing her voice, Ross immediately remembers. "Why bless my soul, it's Phoebe Land. Madame, you know me, I am Joseph Ross."

It is now Phoebe's turn to look askance and then smile. "Captain Ross, forgive me, how could I ever forget your clemency. Without you sir, we would most certainly have perished. These are my two youngest, Robert and Ephraim."

Nodding to the young men, Ross asks: "Are you…returning to the Delaware Madame?"

"No sir, we are on our way to the Upper Lakes. We stop here seeking my son John."

"Then you know where to look Madame, for he has, through hard work and determination, regained a good portion of your family's holdings and has become a respectable citizen of this new republic."

Ross summons a raftsman to bear the Lands across the river then bids them goodbye.

On the other side Phoebe leads her sons up the first bank and away from the river towards a stand of pine.

"Where was the house mam?" Robert asks surveying the surrounding ground.

"Right here," Phoebe says, standing waist-deep in weeds and pointing to a low pile of rocks that was once a chimney. "This is where we lived."

For a moment a flash of fire and the terror and pain associated with the house flares but is quickly quelled and Phoebe, after casting about, leaves the old foundation and sets off toward a nearby cabin.

A tall man in his early 30s bundling beaver pelts in the yard looks up as she approaches. For a moment neither is quite sure if this is a dream or reality.

"John," she calls and he drops his bundle and stares at the grey-haired woman he hasn't seen for fourteen years.

Quickly he runs to her, wraps her in his arms, lays his face on her shoulder and weeps.

Turning to Robert and Ephraim he looks in astonishment and asks. "And are these my little brothers?"

"Indeed they are John, grown now to men."

Some hours later after he has introduced his wife and two daughters and shown off the handsome red barn he's built, John sits at the table with his mother and asks the question that had been looming in his mind from the moment they met.

"Why don't you come back here? I've been able to buy back some of father's property, we can likely get more. Things have changed in Cushetunk, people accept me now. We still have friends here mam. We could start over, there's plenty of…"

Phoebe quiets him by putting her fingers to his lips. "John, you don't understand. Your father can never live on the Delaware again—he was declared a traitor, they meant to hang him. The children and I were driven out of here by Patriots, people who used to be our neighbours. Your brother Abel spent his youth fighting Americans. Our family was nearly destroyed by this war, we can never embrace these people again. We are forever marked as different. Already I've heard what they call you—John Land the Tory—and truly, I don't know how you can bear it."

"I bear it mother, because I must. Yes, they tried to hang me, they left me in gaol, they insult me to my face. Sometimes it makes me boil inside. But Lilly is a good woman, her family accepts me and I believe, in time, what's passed will be forgotten."

There are tears in John's eyes as he speaks and Phoebe reaches out and cradles his hand in hers, casting her eyes downward.

"Maybe for you my son, but your father and I won't live long enough for that to happen."

Early the next morning, John and Phoebe paddle to Big Eddy. While the sun slowly rises they crawl up the steep rocky incline. Finding the sheer face, she directs John and waits as he climbs hand over hand to the cleft she and Kate sought out a dozen years before.

"There an opening just ahead of you," she calls. "Do you see it?"

"Yes, I'm just going into it."

Perhaps a minute later he emerges and calls down, some anxiety in his voice, "Is there a second opening in here? I can't find anything at all."

For 10 minutes John roots frantically in the tiny cave scratching up the dirt and leaves and bits of animal fur left by various creatures seeking shelter over the years before he emerges, fingers torn and bleeding, to announce, "It's gone, someone's taken it."

Back at the eddy where the canoe is tethered, Phoebe puts her hand on John's shoulder and sighs, "There were valuable goods up there, silver plate, cutlery and some fine glass. They were all that's left from the homestead. Now there's only this old quilt."

October, 1791

☙

"Wives and children must tread the hard road."
—Nancy Jean Cameron

It has been one of the rare October days that Land had come to love at the head of the lake. A sharp frost has nipped off the mosquitoes and cleared the air of pollen, leaving a lucid clearness that extends visibility well over the lake. The forest, led by maples and sumacs, has begun to consume itself in a fiery display of reds and yellows. The wild vines hang heavy with grapes. A few bees comb the remaining blooms for nectar. Land has spent the morning winnowing grain and by mid-afternoon, tired of the dust, walked down to the bay to a small wharf that emerges from the cattails. In the burnished warmth of a fall sun he sits, back to a piling, and smokes a pipe.

He has reason to be expansive. He now has 12 acres clear and under cultivation and there is grain and corn enough that he is selling the surplus to Fort Niagara. The cabin now has two rooms and a loft and there is a stable for livestock and a husking peg. He trades furs to Beasley for supplies and with some crude tools makes spinning jennies for his neighbours. The Crown has created the new colony of Upper Canada which guarantees freehold property rights. A Crown survey of the area has been completed and Land's name is on a 300 acre plot between the ridge and the bay. He had written Phoebe the news, telling her to sell the New Brunswick holding and come west. Although he hopes he might see his family again this year, realistically he knows it will likely be spring, at the earliest, before they can arrange passage to the upper country. At times the realization nearly a decade has passed since he's seen his children, deals him a sharp pang but he takes pride knowing he's regained some security for his family. And on one count he has made partial payment on a debt that weighs heavily. He has convinced Ann Morden, the widow of Ralph Morden to move her family to the head of the lake and they are settled on a superior millsite just beyond Coote's sprawling marsh.

On the lake he watches a small sail, perhaps a batteau, move with the wind. In front of him ducks and geese graze the shallows, salmon work toward the spawning streams that ring the bay. The sun, with none of the intensity of summer, is mannered and warm, a respite before the north winds that scour the bay in winter. He watches a fitful breeze stir and ripple the waters and inhales deeply, savouring the scrubbed, fresh water smell.

He has just tapped out his pipe into the water when he notices the batteau has crossed the inlet and is sailing, with the wind, down the bay. Likely belongs to Beasley, Land thinks, probably a load of trade goods destined for the Indians in exchange for furs.

Surveying the bay and the bowl that surrounds it, Land thinks again of the Delaware, where a life full of promise and prosperity, so seemingly settled and ordered, had been turned on its ear and smashed. How the good blood between families and neighbours turned venomous and made him and his family exiles in the land of their birth. But here is a rich, new land quickly filling up with old neighbours. He is beginning to feel the weight of age but there are sons and daughters and indeed, their offspring, eager to put down roots in the new colony. There have been times when the feeling of loss and loneliness were almost more than he could bear but fate and the Crown had dealt a second hand and he has played it wisely.

The old days in Pennsylvania seem now like a distant dream, the edges blurring, fading into the past. Out of chaos and despair he has been delivered onto the fertile shores of a sweet-water sea.

A breeze ripples across the bay, nudging aside the gentle warmth. Land looks up and sees the batteau, now close enough to know it is indeed one of the clumsy freighters that regularly coasts down the lake from the mouth of the Niagara. The deck is piled with gear—barrels, bales, and chests—and there are several people on board but what catches Land's eye is a splash of colour in the bow. A swirl of reds and blues that flashes in the late-afternoon sun.

Land stands, his pipe falling to the wharf, and stares, hardly daring to believe what he is seeing. He closes his eyes and nearly a decade of separation, pain, sorrow and despair, shrinks and falls away. When he opens them again he can clearly see the quilt, a bit faded but still brilliant, wrapped around the shoulders of the handsome, grey-haired woman in the bow. Their eyes meet and she raises a hand to her mouth. Time stops. It is over. It is beginning.

Epilogue

What remains?

Cushetunk today. Nowadays called Milanville (pronounced Mylan-ville) the Pennsylvania village is remarkably unchanged over the past two centuries. The timbered mountains still roll down to the river. The setting, more rustic and rural than one could imagine less than two hours drive from New York City. Fewer than thirty families live in the village. Many descendants of Robert Land and his neighbours—both enemy and friend—still inhabit the area and their memories are long. Loyalist is still a synonym for traitor in many parts of rural Pennsylvania and New York.

Part of the former Land homestead remains a working farm fronting the Delaware. The most likely site of the Land house is now owned by a pair of antique dealers. It's all very tranquil today. John, the only Land to return to the valley is buried in nearby Damascus, Pennsylvania. The fine red house he built in 1794 on his father's former holdings is now the oldest dwelling in the county.

The log jail in Johnsonburg, New Jersey where John Land spent most of the war was built by Samuel Green, father of Stoney Creek pioneer Adam Green and grandfather of Billy Green.

James Quinlan's 1851 book on the pioneers of Minisink says Land eventually discovered who stole the family silver from its hillside hiding place and beat him with a rafter's pole.

There is no family plaque to mark Milanville site. Nothing to acknowledge the part they played in the formative history of both countries. Perhaps there should be.

The site of the Kane family massacre is now a private residence but was, until the mid-'80s, a biker bar. It's still an unquiet place, there's blood in the soil.

Conversely, Hamilton is hugely changed. The wilderness of thick forest, clear water and teeming wildlife is not even a memory. Finding any trace of Robert Land in Hamilton today is almost impossible.

For the best perspective of family holdings, climb to the top of the Wentworth steps and face the lake. Everything from the Mountain to the bay between Sherman and Wellington was Land property.

When Robert Land arrived, the landscape before you was an unbroken canopy of hardwood forest pierced only by the odd mast of white pine. Trace the Land holdings now, beginning at the lake and heading south and behold a vista of junk yards and grim industrial sites. A few tenacious residential pockets, the odd outcrop of scrubby, stubby vegetation.

There are faint echoes in Land Street a two-block eyesore, home to 17 modest houses, cheek-to-jowl with heavy, dockyard, industrial blight. Aged bulk carriers winter in the gun-grey waters now.

Barbed wire and chain link enforce "Keep out!" signs. The place stinks of lake and oil.

Scrub brush and weeds catch the litter and discard of industry. Residential pockets tenaciously, unhappily co-exist with small machine shops.

Down on Barton, kitty-cornered from St. Matthews Avenue in the asphalt of Municipal Parking Lot #79, beside Nick's Auto Service. Most likely this is where Hamilton began.

An expired Chinese restaurant, a T-shirt outlet, an Amity clearance centre. The old Land estate is now a rabbit warren of tiny houses on tiny lots, shoehorned beside one another. Tiny gardens host aged vans bleeding rust.

Evoking ghosts is no easy matter here. You'll search in vain for the terrifying sylvan wilderness that confronted Robert Land 215 years ago.

Easton, Pennsylvania, where Land and Morden were jailed is a lovely small city in the rolling confluence of the Delaware, Lehigh and the Bushkill rivers. The downtown boasts some fine 18th Century buildings. Court house square survives although the building itself was replaced by a Civil War monument. Gallows Hill, less its gallows survives, likely inside the city jail yard that covers the top of the hill and probably the unmarked grave of Ralph Morden.

One of the judges that tried Morden was Thomas McKean, a signatory of the Declaration of Independence. A young British officer in the same jail recorded in his journal that Morden, although only 38 at the time, was an old man.

While charged with treason, Robert Land was nevertheless granted bail, a not-uncommon act during a time when authorities feared the sort of contagious disease associated with close confinement in jails. George Palmer, one of Penn's surveyors and Daniel Skinner, a Cushetunk neighbour stood bail for him and lost it when he skipped.

In New York city the cemetery where William was buried adjoins Trinity Church on Broadway.

The hand of the figurehead on the American frigate, John Hancock was indeed sliced off after the Royal Navy captured the ship. (Upon placing his large and distinctive signature on the Declaration of Independence, Hancock had declared, "There, I guess King George will be able to read that.") Robert Land, according to his court martial testimony, was working in the King's shipyard when the Hancock came in for repair and refit.

The Saint John River Valley Region, part of Nova Scotia when Phoebe Land arrived in 1783, had within a year become the new colony of New Brunswick.

The idyllic picture of the Head-of-the-Lake—the stands of wood and the clear waters of the bay—is not fanciful but drawn entirely from the accounts of 18th Century travellers such as Isaac Weld, Patrick Campbell, Elizabeth Simcoe, Walter Butler and the early surveyors. Bezaleel Tyler, the scourge of the Land family met his untimely end just two months after testifying at Robert Land's court martial. He was reportedly the first killed by Joseph Brant's Volunteers at the battle of Minisink in July 1779, quite possibly by Brant himself.

Edward Hicks, the young Butler's Ranger captured with Land, made good his escape and settled in what is now eastern Ontario after the war. Although he would subsequently claim to have escaped a death sentence, he was in fact sentenced to be kept in "close confinement" for the remainder of the war.

Seven years after Ralph Morden was hanged, Ann Morden, three sons, three daughters, a son-in-law and three grandchildren made the trek to Upper Canada settling in Queenston for three years before moving down the lake to the site of what is now Dundas.

Oziah McCarty married Land's oldest child Abagail and settled on property bought from Brant.

Brant and Land were charter members of the Barton Masonic Lodge.

Robert Land lived through another war with the Americans—the War of 1812. He was 82 when he died in 1818 in the house he'd built on what is now the south side of Barton Street, across from the intersection of St. Matthews. To his wife he left one third of his considerable land holdings, the rest to Robert and Ephraim. The remainder of his children got 20 shillings each, a relatively trifling sum (five days pay for him during the Revolution). Phoebe would die in 1826 at the age of 93. They were buried first on the Barton homestead and then transferred to the family vault at Hamilton Cemetery.

Land's first cabin grew into an imposing two-storey brick structure known as Landholme. Sold by the family in the late 19th Century it became, successively, a boarding house, a convalescent home, a military hospital and finally a children's home before being torn down in 1928.

The stone pillars from Landholme, inscribed with that name, can still be seen fronting the driveway of 341 James Street South in Hamilton.

GLOSSARY

Aanin—Ojibway greeting

Ague fever—Common bush fever, most likely malaria

Almshouse—poorhouse

Andre, John—British officer hanged as a spy in 1780 for his part in the treason of Benedict Arnold

Bannock—unleavened camp bread made of flour, water and lard, often cooked by wrapping around a stick

Bleeding—Deliberate bloodletting commonly practiced by 18th Century surgeons as treatment for many medical conditions

Blueskins—zealous Rebels

Boilsted—maple

Burgoyne, John—British general who led 8,000 troops on ill-fated invasion of colonies in 1777

Bouwerie—dutch farm

Bowse—pull or haul hard

Capote—Woolen blanket coat

Carleton, Guy—Army officer, twice Governor of Quebec

Clinton, Sir Henry—Britain's ranking military commander in North America 1778-82

Committees of Public Safety—Local groups in the 13 colonies appointed to administer laws and justice in the wake of the collapse of established authority at the beginning of the Revolution

Declaration of Independence—Formal declaration by colonies in 1776 cutting all administrative and judicial ties with Great Britain. The document destroyed any hope of conciliation and opened the door for alliance with France

Delaware Water Gap—Near Stroudsburg, Pennsylvania where the Delware River cuts through Kittatinny Mountain.

Fundament—buttocks, rectum

Geldsoldaten—German for mercenaries, literally "gold soldiers"

Gorget—a shell-shaped symbol of military rank worn around the neck

Goshen—Village in southeast New York

Haldimand, Frederick—Army officer, governor of Quebec responsible for establishing Loyalist refugees in what is now Ontario

Hemp—used to make rope

Hobnails—vanilla-raisin cookies

Hoe cake—cornmeal cake originally cooked on hoe or fire rake in open fire

Hominy—Algonquian for hulled, ground corn, preserved by parching or drying with wood lye

Jolly boat—ship's boat

King's Mountain—Ridge between North and South Carolina, site of decisive Rebel victory over large Loyalist and British force, October, 1780. Major influence in breaking British power in the South

Levellers—Rebel mobs

Mingo—chamber pot

Night-soil—human excrement dumped from buildings into the street

Ostler—stable hand

Oriskany—Village near Utica, New York, site of 1777 ambush of American militia. A tactical Crown victory in a losing campaign.

Pearl ash—Obtained from treatment of wood ash, used to make soap

Poltroon—coward

Pontiac—Ottawa chief, led rebellion against the British in 1763

Prison hulks—decommissioned naval ships used to hold prisoners

Putrid fever—typhus, spotted fever

Robinson, Beverley—Spymaster, head of British military intelligence in New York

Samp or nasaump—coarsely ground corn or porridge made from it

Sandy Hook—New Jersey peninsula five miles south of New York's Lower Bay

Shad—saltwater fish that ascends rivers to spawn

Skinners—Rebel outlaws

Simsbury—former copper mine near Hartford, called the Catacomb of Connecticut used to hold British and Loyalist prisoners during the Revolution.

Simcoe, John Graves—Commander of Queen's Rangers, one of the more effective Loyalist units, first Lieutenant-Governor of Upper Canada

Slash—marsh

Saratoga—Upper New York, site in 1777 of first major American victory of Revolution, considered turning point in war

Snickerdoodles—cinnamon-walnut cookies

Sot weed—tobacco

Sow-gelders—An insulting reference to incompetent physicians. Gelding refers to castration, a sow is a female pig.

Spinning jennies—spinning wheels

Steuben—Prussian officer, inspector-general of Continental army

Swale—A low, wet piece of land

Tar or jack tar—Royal Navy sailor

Tricorn—three-cornered hat

Waabshkiiyed—Ojibway for pale face

Wake-me-up—Bush tea made of green tea, chicory, acorns and maple sugar

Wequatetong—Ojibway for bay

West Point—Strategic Hudson River fort, now site of famous military academy

Wyoming and Cherry Valley—Frontier settlements in Pennsylvania and New York attacked and overrun by Loyalist units in 1778. Commonly referred to as massacres in the US

BIBLIOGRAPHY

UNPUBLISHED PRIMARY SOURCES

Historical Society of Wisconsin. Madison, WI
Joseph Brant Papers. Draper, Lyman Copeland F series, 15 v.

National Archives, Ottawa, ON
British Headquarters Papers, New York 1774-1783 (Manuscript Group 23)

National Archives of Canada, Ottawa, ON
Haldimand Papers. (Manuscript Group 21)

Ontario, Department of Lands and Forests, Map and Survey Division, Toronto, ON
Field Notes from Early Surveyor's Notebooks.

Pennsylvania Archives, Harrisburg, PA
Records of the Supreme Court of Pennsylvania Courts of Oyer and Terminer Docket 1778 - 1786, v. 1

U.S. Library of Congress, Manuscript Division, Washington DC
George Washington Papers.

University of Michigan, William L. Clements Library, Ann Arbor, MI
Clinton Papers.

PUBLISHED PRIMARY SOURCES, RECORDS, DIARIES ETC

Balderson, Marion; Syrett, David, editors. *The Lost War: Letters from British Officers during the American Revolution.* New York, Horizon Press, 1975.

Bartram, John, Lewis Evans and Conrad Weiser. *A Journey from Pennsylvania to Onondaga in 1743.* Barre, MA: Imprint Society, 1973.

Benians, E. A., editor. *A Journal by Thomas Hughes for his Amusement.* Cambridge: 1947.

Black List: A List of Tories Attainted of High Treason. Philadelphia: McKean & Dallas, 1802.

Butler, Walter. "Journal of An Expedition along the North Shore of Lake Ontario, 1799", edited by James F. Kenney, **Canadian Historical Review**. Dec. 1920: pp 381-391.

Campbell, Patrick. *Travels in the Interior Inhabited Parts of North America in the Years 1791 and 1792.* Edited by H.H. Langton. Toronto: The Champlain Society, 1937.

Clinton, George. *The Public Papers of George Clinton.* Edited by Hugh Hastings. Albany, NY: State of New York, 1900 War of the Revolution Series, v. 2, 3 and 4.

Commager, Henry Steele and Morris, Richard B., editors *The Spirit of 'Seventy-Six': The Story of the American Revolution as told by Participants.* New York: Harper & Row, 1975.

Crary, Catherine S., editor. *The Price of Loyalty: Tory Writings from the Revolutionary Era.* New York: McGraw Hill, 1973.

Cruikshank Ernest, editor. *Petition for Grants of Lands, 1792-96.* Ontario Historical Society Papers and Records, Volume 24. Toronto: 1927.

Gerlach, Larry R., editor. *The American Revolution: New York as a Case Study.* Belmont CA: Wadsworth Publishing, 1972.

Goldie, John. *Diary of a Journey through Upper Canada, 1819.* Toronto: Privately published, 1967.

Jones, Augustus. *Surveyors' Letters.* Toronto: Ontario Department of Lands and Forests.

New York. State Historian. *Second Annual Report.* Albany: State Legislature 1897.

New York Genealogical and Biographical Society *Records of Trinity Church Parrish* v. 1, New York: 1937, pp. 94.136.

Norton, John. *The Journal of Major John Norton 1816.* Edited by Carl Klinck and James Talman. Toronto: The Champlain Society, 1970.

Ontario. Bureau of Archives. *Report, 1903-1904.* Toronto: The Bureau, 1905.

Priest, Josiah. *The Captivity and Sufferings of General Freegift Patchin.* Albany: Garland Publishing, 1977. Facsimile reprint of 1833 edition.

Sabine, William H. W. *Historical Memoirs of William Smith.* New York: Arno Press, 1971.

Sabine, William H. W. *The New York Diary of Lieutenant Jabez Fitch.* New York: Arno Press 1954.

Segar, Nathaniel, *A Brief Narrative of the Captivity and Sufferings of Lt. Nathan'l Segar.* New York: Garland 1977. Reprint of 1825 Oxford Bookstore edition.

Skinner, Nathan. *The Nathan Skinner Manuscript.* Edited by Arthur N. Meyers Narrowsburgh NY: Delaware Valley Press, 1970.

Smith, Michael. *Geographical View of the Province of Upper Canada and Promiscuous Remarks on the Government.* New York: 1813.

The Pennsylvania Gazette. April 21, 1779.

The Susquehanna Company Papers. Edited by Robert J. Taylor. Ithaca, NY: Cornell University Press 1968. v. 6, 1774-1775.

Walton, William. *A Narrative of the Captivity and Sufferings of Benjamin Gilbert and his Family Who were Surprised by the Indians on the Frontiers of Pennsylvania in the Spring, 1780.* New York: Garland, 1975. Reprint of the 1784 edition.

Washington, George. *The Writings of George Washington from Original Manuscript Sources, 1745-1799.* Edited by John C. Fitzpatrick. Washington, DC: U.S. Government Printing Office, Washington.

Weld, Isaac. *Travels through the States of North America and the provinces of Upper and Lower Canada during the years 1795, 1796 and 1797.* New York: Johnson, 1968. Reprint of 1807 Stockdale edition.

PUBLISHED SECONDARY SOURCES

Allen, Robert S. *His Majesty's Indian Allies.* Toronto: Dundurn Press, 1992.

Ballantine, Betty and Ballantine, Ian, editors. *The Native Americans: An Illustrated History.* Atlanta: Turner Publishing, 1993.

Banwell, Selwyn. *The Loyalist.* Toronto: Rous and Mann, Toronto, 1934.

Barck, Oscar Theodore. *New York City During the War for Independence.* New York: Columbia University Press, 1931.

Bell, D. G. *Early Loyalist Saint John.* Saint John, NB: New Ireland Press 1983.

Boatner, Mark Mayo. *Encyclopedia of the American Revolution.* New York: David McKay, 1966.

Bray, William. *The Development of Vegetation in New York State.* New York State College, 1930.

Brown, Dorothy I. *A Loyalist's Legacy: The Family of Robert Land.* Mississauga, ON: The Author, 1985.

Brown, Wallace. *The King's Friends: The Composition and Motives of the American Loyalist Claimants.* Providence, RI: Brown University Press, 1965.

Buel, Joy Day; Buel, Richard Jr. *The Way of Duty—A Woman and her Family in Revolutionary America.* New York: W.W. Norton, 1984.

Burbank, James. W. *Cushetunk 1754-1784.* Callicoon, NY: Sullivan County Democrat 1975.

Calhoon, Robert McCluer. *The Loyalists in Revolutionary America 1760-1781.* New York: Harcourt Brace Jovanovich, 1965.

Campbell, Marjorie Freeman. *A Mountain and a City. The Story of Hamilton.* Toronto: McClelland & Stewart, 1966.

Chambers, Robert W. *The Maid-at-Arms.* New York: Harper & Brothers 1902.

Coleman, John M. *Thomas McKean: Forgotten Leader of the Revolution.* Rockaway, NJ: American Faculty Press, 1975.

Coleman, John M. "Robert Land and Some Frontier Skirmishes". *Ontario History* 48 (no. 2, 1956): pp. 47–62.

Coleman, John M. "The Treason of Ralph Morden and Robert Land". *Pennsylvania Magazine of History and Biography* 79, (No. 4 October 1955): pp. 439-451.

Cruikshank, Ernest. *Butler's Rangers and the Settlement of Niagara.* Niagara Falls, ON: Lundy's Lane Historical Society, 1988. Reprint of Welland Tribune edition.

Densmore, Frances. *Indian Use of Wild Plants.* Ohsweken, ON: Iroqrafts, 1993. Reprint of 1928 Smithsonian Institution edition.

Edmonds, Walter D. *Drums Along the Mohawk.* New York: Bantam Books, 1963.

Farmer, Dennis and Carol. *The King's Bread, 2d Rising. Cooking at Niagara, 1726-1815.* Youngstown, NY: Old Fort Niagara Association, 1989.

Gates, Lillian F. *Land Policies in Upper Canada.* Toronto: University of Toronto Press, 1968.

Glover, Douglas. *The Life and Times of Captain N.* Toronto: McClelland and Stewart, 1993.

Graymont, Barbara. *The Iroquois in the American Revolution.* Syracuse, NY: Syracuse University Press, 1972.

Grose, Captain Francis. *A Classical Dictionary of the Vulgar Tongue.* Edited by Eric Partridge, New York: Doset Press, 1992. Reprint of 1796 edition.

Halliday, W. E. D. *A Forest Classification for Canada.* Ottawa: Canadian Forestry Service, 1937.

Hoffman, Ronald; Albert, Peter J. editors. *Women in the Age of the American Revolution.* Charlottesville, VA: University Press of Virginia, 1989.

Hosie, R. C. *Native Trees of Canada.* Ottawa: Canadian Forestry Service, 1973.

Huey, Lois M. and Bonnie Pulis. *Molly Brant: A Legacy of Her Own.* Youngstown, NY: Old Fort Niagara Association, 1997.

Johnson, Michael G. *American Woodland Indians.* London: Osprey, 1990.

Jones, Rufus M. *The Quakers in the American Colonies.* New York: Russell & Russell, 1962.

Kelsay, Isabel Thompson. *Joseph Brant 1743-1807: Man of Two Worlds.* Syracuse: Syracuse University Press, 1984.

Kirby, William. *Annals of Niagara.* Niagara Falls ON: Lundy's Lane Historical Society, 1896.

Lamoureux, W. John. "Giant Trees of the Gardens" *The Gardens' Bulletin.* 25 (March 1971) pp. 1-6. Royal Botanical Gardens, Hamilton, ON.

Lederer, Richard M. *Colonial American English.* Essex, CT: Verbatim, 1985.

Levy, Barry. *Quakers and the American Family: British Settlement in the Delaware Valley.* New York: Oxford University Press, 1988.

Loewer, Peter. *Letters to Sarah: A Year in the Life of a Settler's Family, 1769-1770.* Narrowsburgh, NY: Sullivan County Public Works, 1989.

Lowell, Edward J. *The Hessians and the other German Auxiliaries of Great Britain in the Revolutionary War.* New York: Harper & Brothers, 1884.

MacKinnon, Neil. *This Unfriendly Soil – The Loyalist Experience in Nova Scotia 1783-1791.* Montreal: McGill-Queen's University Press, 1986.

Mathews, Hazel C. *The Mark of Honour.* Toronto: University of Toronto, 1965.

Mekeel, Arthur J. *The Relation of the Quakers to the American Revolution.* Washington, DC: University Press of America, 1979.

Meyers, Arthur N. *Milanville, The Center of Cushetunk.* Milanville PA: Delaware Valley Press, 1964.

Minhinnick, Jeanne. *At Home in Upper Canada.* Toronto: Clarke, Irwin, 1970.

Moore, Christopher. *The Loyalists: Revolution, Exile, Settlement.* Toronto: Macmillan of Canada, 1984.

Norris, Darrell. "Household and Transiency in a Loyalist Township." *Social History.* 23 (November 1980).

Patterson, Gilbert C. "Land Settlement in Upper Canada 1783-96" *Ontario Archives. Sixteenth Report.* (1921)

Peattie, Donald Culross *A Natural History of Trees of Eastern and Central North America.* New York: Houghton Mifflin, 1991.

Potter-MacKinnon, Janice. *While the Women Only Wept: Loyalist Refugee Women.* Montreal: McGill-Queen's University Press 1993.

Pratt, Fletcher. *The Navy A History: The Story of a Service in Action.* Garden City, NY: 1941

Quinlan, James Eldridge. *History of Sullivan County.* Liberty NY: Beebe & Morgans, 1873.

Quinlan, James Eldridge. *Tom Quick The Indian Slayer and the Pioneers of Minisink and Wawasink.* Monticello NY: DeVoe and Quinlan, 1851.

Riordan, Liam. "Identity and Revolution: Everyday Life and Crisis in Three Delaware River Towns" *Pennsylvania History.* 64 (winter 1997) pp. 56-91.

Robertson, J. Ross editor. *The Diary of Mrs John Graves Simcoe.* Toronto: Ontario Publishing, 1934.

Roland, Charles G. "Health and Disease Among the Early Loyalists in Upper Canada". *Canadian Medical Association Journal* 128 (March 1, 1983) pp. 687-595.

Siebert, Wilbur H. "The Loyalists and Six Nations in the Niagara Peninsula" *Royal Society of Canada Transactions* 9 (1915) pp.79-129.

Swiggett, Howard. *War Out of Niagara.* New York: Columbia University Press, 1933

Selig, Robert A. "America The Ungrateful" *American Heritage,* February/March 1997, pp.101-106.

Sivertson, Barbara J. and Covey, Barabara L., *The Legend of Cushetunk.* Bowie, MD: Heritage Books. 1993.

Talman, James J., editor. *Loyalist Narratives from Upper Canada.* Toronto: The Champlain Society, 1946.

Tebbel, John. *Turning the World Upside Down.* New York: Orion Books, 1993.

Thomas, Earle. *The Three Faces of Molly Brant.* Kingston: Quarry Press, 1996.

Trueblood, D. Elton. *The People Called Quakers.* New York: Harper and Row, 1966.

Upton, Leslie, editor. *The United Empire Loyalists: Men and Myths.* Toronto: Copp Clark, 1967.

Van Doren, Carl. *Secret History of the American Revolution.* New York: Viking Press, 1968.

Waldman, Carl. *Atlas of the North American Indian.* New York: Facts on File, 1985.

Wallace, Paul A. W. *Indian Paths of Pennsylvania.* Harrisburg, PA: The Pennsylvania Historical and Museum Commission, 1965.

Watt, Gavin K. *The Burning of the Valleys.* Toronto: Dundurn Press, 1997.

Webster, Rev. T. *The New Dominion Monthly.* February, 1869.

Wertenbaker, Thomas Jefferson. *Father Knickerbocker Rebels: New York City during the Revolution.* New York: Charles Scribner's Sons, 1948.

Wright, E. C. *The Loyalists of New Brunswick.* Fredericton, NB: privately printed, 1985.

UNPUBLISHED SECONDARY SOURCES

Stevens, Paul Lawrence. *His Majesty's "Savage" Allies: British Policy and the Northern Indians During the Revolutionary War.* Buffalo: State Univeristy of New York, 1984 Doctoral thesis.

Young, Henry J. *The Treatment of Loyalists in Pensinsula.* Baltimore, MD: John Hopkins University, 1955. Dissertation.